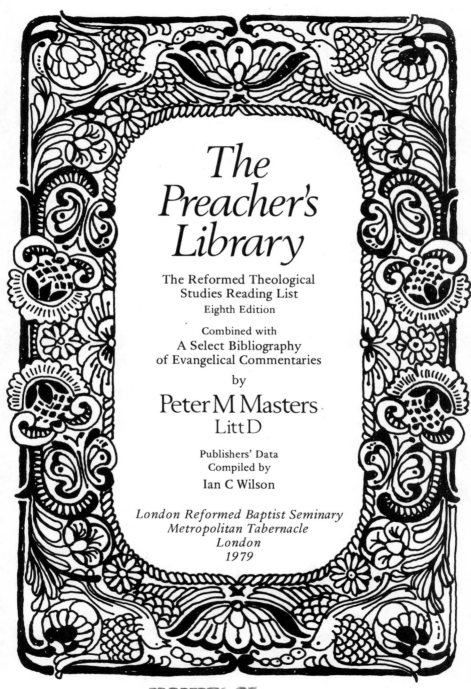

The Preacher's Library

The Reformed Theological
Studies Reading List

Eighth Edition

Combined with

A Select Bibliography
of Evangelical Commentaries

by

Peter M Masters
Litt D

Publishers' Data
Compiled by

Ian C Wilson

London Reformed Baptist Seminary
Metropolitan Tabernacle
London
1979

By the same author:

Men of Destiny
Men of Purpose
Physician of Souls
Guidance

Published and Printed by
Wakeman Publishers Ltd, London EC2
for
The Metropolitan Tabernacle
Elephant & Castle
London SE1 6SD

The Preacher's Library
Contents

Key to Abbreviations

BT   Banner of Truth Trust
EP   Evangelical Press
GSBT   Gospel Standard Baptist Trust
H&S   Hodder & Stoughton
Klock   Klock & Klock
P&I   Pickering & Inglis
P&R   Presbyterian & Reformed
St.AP   St Andrew Press

The price given for books from United States publishers is that fixed by the importing wholesaler (or is calculated by the wholesaler's "mark-up" formula). The "TB" price alongside is that listed by The Tabernacle Bookshop, Metropolitan Tabernacle, London, which by direct importing and special purchasing arrangements consistently achieves a lower price.

Acknowledgements

I would like to express my great appreciation to the principals of several publishing houses in the United States for their warm hospitality and considerable help in providing review copies and advance information of publications. Particular thanks are due to Mr Richard Baker of Baker Book House, Mr Peter Gunther, Director of Moody Press, Mr Robert Kregel of Kregel Publications, and Dr Bob De Vries, Chief Executive of the Zondervan Corporation.   PMM

Reformed Theological Studies Reading List

Introduction

Study to show thyself approved unto God, a workman that needeth not to be ashamed, rightly dividing the Word of Truth. (2 Tim 2.15)

The *Reformed Theological Studies Reading List* recommends works which, in the opinion of the compiler, are the best available in print for all the departments of reading necessary to pastors, preachers and Christian workers, (with the exception of the study of biblical languages).

The word "best" ought to be briefly explained. By it is meant the works which achieve the best balance of the following essential qualities: —

Scriptural soundness
Reasonable brevity and concise style
Liveliness
Readiness to cover practical pastoral implications
Style of presentation which is most suggestive to preachers
A method of presentation which stimulates the faculties of the reader

The aim has always been to sift out books answering, as far as possible, these requirements. Does a book help me to be a better practical counsellor? Does it increase my usefulness as a teacher? Does it challenge and inspire me as a preacher of the precious everlasting Gospel of Christ? Will it increase my usefulness to my flock — or will it encourage me to be dry, complex, old-fashioned, esoteric and so on?

Some famous weighty tomes which friends always expect to appear on these annual lists are often set aside because a less wordy (if not so renowned) author has covered the same material in fewer pages and with more application and a more enjoyable style. It is surely much better to have volumes one actually reads, than famous "heavies" which remain unread, mocking us from the shelves.

We are very happy to see the great fall in the cost of American books for there are so very many US titles of vital importance to us. Indeed, many great British classics (as you will see) are now only published by leading American publishers.

Generally speaking the list includes many alternative titles in each section so there is overlap and duplication. It also includes reference to many works which will appear during 1979 to give preachers a better familiarity with the world of evangelical publishing.

I take full responsibility for the comments about each book — which are in no case derived from publishers' 'blurbs' but are all (except in the case of a few future announcements) based on a personal review of the work. If another person's opinion is quoted in a comment, it is because I fully concurred with the words quoted and could not improve on them.

Just a word about the use of the *Reformed Theological Studies Reading List* by men in different parts of the world who are preparing for Christian service by personal study. The selection of ninety-two titles (not including commentaries) which constitutes the intensive study course at the *London Reformed Baptist Seminary* is marked out on the List Ⓢ. You are always welcome to correspond with the Seminary Registrar for advice or literature. The Seminarians attend regular Tutorials alongside the reading course.

It will be seen from the RTSRL that our Seminary has, in effect, an enormous "faculty" of remarkable calibre! It includes scholars and preachers of renown from many Evangelical traditions and out of every period of church history from the Reformation. We are able to summon to our lecture theatre long-buried worthies from times of Reformation and revival.

This is why we view intensive reading — not as a second-rate expedient — but as the finest method of study that there is.

Who could raise a faculty to match ours? What seminary student anywhere else could command the lecturer at will to slow down, stop, repeat a sentence — or even the last twenty minutes? Where else can a student rise in the night, produce a nineteenth century theology professor from a cupboard, and proceed to hear his lecture? Or, where else can the great Dr Owen be resurrected and persuaded to omit his repetitions and Latin quotations?

Our twentieth century has its "last age" problems, but it has this great blessing — a mighty heritage of literature. So to all who study by reading, whether students, preachers, missionaries — never be tempted to undervalue that heritage. Yours is the noblest and the best institution of them all.

PMM

Therefore, my beloved brethren, be ye stedfast, unmoveable, always abounding in the work of the Lord, forasmuch as ye know that your labour is not in vain in the Lord. (1 Cor 15.58)

The Preacher's Library — Introduction

Doctrine–General

A Body of Divinity Ⓢ   BT
Thomas Watson

Seventeenth century classic revised for text-book use at Spurgeon's Pastors' College. Still the finest introduction to our system of theology and the essential starting point. Watson has the best treatment of the Fall in print; his work is heartsearching and applied throughout. (Baker will soon have a paperback including The Ten Commandments and the Lord's Prayer. While having a low price, it will be photolithographed from a nineteenth century edition having small print and many wrong Scripture references. This Banner reset edition sounds much better). 316 pages, cloth, £2.50

Systematic Theology Ⓢ   BT
L Berkhof

The very best Reformed, one-volume systematic theology. No serious Christian worker should be without it. Textual approach very strong. (We naturally do not endorse everything here. Dr Berkhof was Presbyterian in the areas of baptism, church government and theocratic covenant and followed the 'Gap Theory' in his analysis of creation.) 784 pages, cloth, £4.50.

The Holy War Ⓢ   Moody
John Bunyan

This great allegory brings the deepest and most difficult theological problems into clear focus. The fall of man, the origin of sin, freewill and so on succumb to its brilliant picture-language. The town of "mansoul" — its rebellion and liberation also provides the best possible insight into God's work in the soul of man for Christian workers. Two editions of Holy War are now available here — the Baker reprint of an old edition and this Moody reset edition. It has an introduction by Wilbur Smith and has been expertly but gently updated in punctuation — without words being changed (like the Penguin Pilgrim's Progress). This greatly improves the reading flow. 378 pages, paper, £5.10, TB £2.50.

Elemental Theology Ⓢ   Zondervan
Emery H Bancroft

Prof Bancroft's excellent systematic theology has been in print for over thirty years. Though not wholly Reformed in places and premillennial on the last things, it is Calvinistic in soteriology. The unique value of this work is that it bridges the gap between

Berkhof and the pew. Prof Bancroft takes vital doctrines and analyses them under the very headings which will suggest much for preached messages. Preachers and teachers will therefore be greatly inspired and assisted by this treatment. 399 pages, cloth, £6.95, TB £4.95.

Institutes of the Christian Religion   Eerdmans
John Calvin

This 2-volume edition is the Henry Beveridge translation of 1845. Unabridged with foreword by the late Prof John Murray. The 1286 pages are very modestly priced. Kivar, the set, £6.20, TB £4.70.

The Works of Jonathan Edwards   BT

Vol 1 — Memoir of Edwards; Freedom of the Will; Original Sin; The Religious Affections; a Narrative of Surprising Conversions, and a History of the Work of Redemption. In the latter "Edwards has given us a truly Christ-centred Body of Divinity. He uses his vast powers to demonstrate that the whole of history right up to the coming of Christ is all subservient to, and part of, this great plan of Redemption. It is unique." — David Fountain. Vol 2 — The Distinguishing Marks of a Work of the Spirit of God, and the Diary of David Brainerd. Cloth, 2 Vols, £7 each.

The Godhead

The Trinity Ⓢ   Kregel
E H Bickersteth

Bickersteth's unique treatment of the Trinity, complete with proof-texts; parallel column presentation of the persons of the Godhead, and extensive references. There is nothing quite like it. 182 pages, paper, £1.80, TB £1.50.

Attributes of God   Baker
A W Pink

A W Pink is at his very best on this great theme. To extend and deepen one's understanding of the attributes, is to lay the best foundation for all other doctrine, ministry and methodology. Pink is excellent and gives the finest example of how to explain and teach this material. 96 pages, paper, £1.50, TB £1.15.

Gleanings in the Godhead Ⓢ   Moody
A W Pink

A much bigger version of the above which (in case binding) will be preferred by many. A magnificent book. 192 pages, cloth, £4.40, TB £3.40.

Names of God in Holy Scripture   Kregel
A Jukes

The most famous work on the names of God. The significance of Jehovah, El Shaddai etc., is here brought out as the Divine Names of both testaments are expounded. A very wordy book, but the intrepid reader will appreciate the strikingly original thought which Jukes never fails to produce. 226 pages, paper, £2.15, TB £1.70.

The Lord Jesus Christ

The Suffering Saviour ⑤   Moody
F W Krummacher

The study of a work such as this is infinitely more profitable than the study of a modern treatment of the life of Christ. This most moving classic is absolutely vital to Christian workers and will be found invaluable for prescribing to others — particularly believers under heavy assault. (See comment under Commentaries, New Testament.) This is not the Baker reprint but the fine Moody Wycliffe edition. 444 pages, paper, £5.10, TB £2.50.

Seven Sayings of the Saviour on the Cross ⑤   Baker
A W Pink

Also listed under Commentaries, New Testament, this study is again far more valuable to preachers than the anaemic material of present day, neo-evangelical academics. 134 pages, paper,   90p, TB 70p.

The Atonement of Christ ⑤   Baker
Francis Turrettin

Turrettin's "Institutes" influenced the Princetonians (and the Hodge family in particular) more than anything else. This portion is a classic and makes easier (and more moving) reading than Charles Hodge's later elaboration of the same material. Listed for "further study". 207 pages, paper, £3.05, TB £2.35.

The Life and Times of Jesus the Messiah   Eerdmans
Alfred Edersheim

We prefer this grand old work to anything modern. If readers must have a life of Christ this is the one. Recent efforts (Guthrie, etc) do not compare, and they take the absurdities of liberal "scholarship" far too seriously. See comment under Commentaries New Testament. 828 pages, cloth, £8.50, TB £6.50.

Christ in the Old Testament   **Moody**
James A Borland

This new study of the theophanies from a sound Baptist seminary lecturer is intended for pastors and teachers. It will appear in December 1978 and will be the subject of a RTSRL Review Sheet. 192 pages, paper, £3.25, TB £2.35.

The Klaas Schilder Trilogy   **Baker**

We feel too long and 'overdone' but others think it is highly suggestive. The Klock edition is very expensive (casebound at £24.85 from EP). The Baker paperback vols are, if anything, stronger and better at (the set) £15.50, TB £11.95.

The Holy Spirit

A Help to the Study of the Holy Spirit Ⓢ   **Baker**
W E Biederwolf

Dr Biederwolf issued this exceptional book in 1903 to counteract the many confusing assertions being made by Murray, Campbell-Morgan and other leading writers, about the Holy Spirit. His study is as positive and humble as its title. He gives the student his "homework" ready done, assembling all the references to the Holy Spirit: baptism and filling etc. Highly recommended as the finest work of its kind. Has outstanding chapters on the Sealing; Anointing; Communion; Baptism and Filling of the Spirit. 127 pages. Out of print but due to be reissued in 1979.

The Holy Spirit — His Gifts and Power Ⓢ   **Kregel**
John Owen

Another completely successful condensation of a renowned classic. Owen's original volumes on the Spirit — the ultimate study — are weighed down by repetitions, digressions and Latin quotations. Fifty years ago a great (and loyal) Owenite scholar took the most sympathetic of scalpels and pruned out all the tedious matter. The result is the whole of Owen's reasoning on the Holy Spirit in one magnificent volume. Owen's highly important chapters on the means of sanctification are now clear and flowing. 356 pages, paper, £2.45, TB £1.95.

Holy Spirit in the Old Testament Ⓢ   Zondervan
Leon Wood

This survey deserves to be much better known in the UK. Let the late Prof Wood guide you to all the references to the Spirit in the Old Testament. The Trinity is not after all a New Testament doctrine but a whole Bible doctrine. A most important survey and very readable. 160 pages, paper, £2.50, TB £1.85.

Tongues, to Speak or not to Speak Ⓢ   Moody
D Burdick

Donald Burdick was once a Pentecostalist minister (now Baptist). He therefore puts the case against tongues with great gentleness, balance and insight. Very well done. 94 pages, paper, £1.20, TB 95p.

The Modern Tongues Movement Ⓢ   Baker
R G Gromacki

Dr Gromacki's work is commended more for its unique treatment of the history of tongues-speaking, especially outside Christian circles. The great prevalence of tongues even in pagan religions will surprise many. Care, the book hits hard and its intermittent harsh tone make it less suitable for prescribing to those troubled by these matters. Nevertheless, one of the best available studies. (pp 72-74 will not command much agreement). 183 pages, paper, £1.50, TB £1.35.

New Testament Teaching on Tongues   Kregel
M F Unger

Typically clear and easy presentation by Dr Unger, defending the non-charismatic position. 175 pages, paper, £1.20, TB 95p.

The Holy Spirit at Work Today   Moody
John F Walvoord

A useful summary of the work of the Spirit, though the chapters are very brief. The description of spiritual gifts under the heads Temporary and Used Today is good. 63 pages, paper, £1.05, TB 75p.

Holy Spirit Baptism   Paternoster
A A Hoekema

A head-on collision with the charismatic case by the Professor of Systematic Theology at Calvin Theological Seminary, Grand Rapids. The Neo-Pentecostal teaching is reviewed, then contrasted with the biblical teaching on Spirit baptism and tongues-speaking. The gifts, fruit and fulness of the Spirit are well covered. The style is rather blunt but very lively and easy to follow. Important reading. 101 pages, paper, £1.00.

Tongues, Healing and You — Baker
Don Hillis

Of all the popular works, this has most to say about healing from the non-charismatic position. It is very well handled. This 112 page paperback has recently gone out of print but will, hopefully, reappear in 1979.

The Holy Spirit — Baker
A W Pink

A W Pink can be relied upon to take an original approach to the presentation of the Doctrine of the Spirit. This is a good and very practical study but it should take its place behind writers previously listed. Cloth, £3.25, TB £2.25.

The Person and Ministry of the Holy Spirit Ⓢ — Baker
Edwin Palmer

A very thorough yet warm and readable work from Dr Palmer, an esteemed Reformed scholar who has been the Principal of the New York Bible Society's New International Version of the Bible. This is highly applied and the chapters on sanctification, guidance and prayer will set a great example to teachers of the Word. Cloth, £3.80, TB £2.85.

Note

We particularly point to Owen for the best treatment of Sanctification and also refer readers to the fine work on this subject by J W Sanderson, "The Fruit of the Spirit" listed under Pastoral Counselling. Edwin Palmer handles the subjective side of things admirably.

The Five Points

The Five Points of Calvinism Ⓢ — Baker
D N Steele & C C Thomas

This little book is our selection as best on the Points and includes fully quoted Scriptures for each one. Weaknesses occur, eg p 39, para 2 asserts as definite a matter hotly debated among Calvinists. Also man's unwillingness is repeatedly attributed to his inability, whereas the latter is part and parcel of the former. This is a surprising flaw, but in spite of this, and one or two similar errors, this book is the clearest of its kind. Paper, £1.10, TB 80p.

Salvation is Forever Ⓢ   Moody
R G Gromacki

The Final Perseverance of the Saints is a doctrine of incalculable comfort and encouragement to Christian people. But how are preachers to deal with the "problem" passages of Scripture, which often seem to imply the opposite? Dr Gromacki's book stands alone in tackling these passages and while there is reservation among Reformed pastors concerning some of the arguments, this is on the whole a powerful and richly suggestive work which will stimulate and help all preachers. 188 pages, paper, £1.85, TB £1.45.

Bondage of the Will Ⓢ   Baker
Martin Luther

In this classic dispute, Luther homes on man's will and the true extent of the fall as the point on which the whole Reformation argument turned. To grasp the arguments of this work is an essential task for serious readers of theology. This Baker edition is well reprinted from the old English Sovereign Grace edition by Coles. Though older than the translation issued at £3.50 by James Clarke, it is less stilted. 419 pages, paper, £1.90, TB £1.45.

Eternal Security   Baker
A W Pink

To choose between Pink and Prof Gromacki is difficult for each work has its merits and material not contained in the other. We prefer Gromacki for the coverage of problem passages. Paper, £1.90, TB £1.40.

Baptism

Should Infants be Baptised? Ⓢ   Baker
T E Watson

First issued in England in 1962 now only available from the USA. The author presents the case against infant baptism by quoting paedo-baptists against themselves. There is a fine brief section disposing of the oft-stated error that the early Christian writers accepted paedo-baptism and a good section on the covenant approach. Brief and highly recommended, 108 pages, paper, £1.50, TB £1.15.

Doctrine — Baptism

Baptizein Ⓢ   **Kregel**
T J Conant

The significance of this classic must not be missed. Professor Conant in a lively work translates and presents every passage of biblical and classical literature in which the 'baptize' verb is used to show that it has never changed its ground meaning "to dip — immerse — plunge". (The review of usage extends to the Catholic writers of the 13th Century.) Of great value to Baptist preachers. 192 pages, cloth, £3.40, TB £2.30.

Baptism — the Heaven Drawn Picture Ⓢ   **Wakeman**
Peter Masters

This booklet considers baptism entirely in terms of what the symbolism portrays. Precisely why should a believer be baptized? Who benefits, and how? The booklet seeks to answer just such questions and is now produced at a price which makes it possible for churches to make it available to those contemplating baptism. 16 page booklet, 5p.

Angels & Demons

Angels, Elect and Evil   **Moody**
C F Dickason

A modern study of the powers (and limitations) of angels and demons. Highly dispensational, but much important material. 240 pages, paper, £2.15, TB £1.70.

What Demons Can Do to Saints Ⓢ   **Moody**
M F Unger

Dr Unger has changed (for the worse) his views since his earlier work 25 years ago, and now believes demons can possess believers. Nevertheless this work is the best presentation of the issues for pastors (case notes excepted!) 204 pages, cloth, £4.25, TB £3.40.

The Word of God

The Inspiration and Authority of the Scriptures Ⓢ   **Moody**
Rene Pache

Another foundational, essential work for pastoral-studies readers. A very concise and readable treatment of inspiration, its necessity, its "mechanics", the canon, documents etc. Leaves no definition or argument out, and yet is probably the most straightforward and enjoyable of all the larger books of its kind. 249 pages, cloth, £5.00, TB £3.85.

The Saviour and the Scriptures Ⓢ   Baker
Robert Lightner

We are very glad to see Dr Bob Lightner's spirited defence of the Word back in print. The Dallas scholar follows the direction of his title, showing how the Lord authenticated the Old Testament, promised the New and clothed all with complete authority. He presents this material better than anyone else. A most significant book with a powerful passage on neo-evangelicalism. Preachers will value the arrangement of points as a help to teaching this theme. 176 pages, paper, £2.45, TB £1.85.
(See works vindicating Scripture under "Apologetics").

Divine Inspiration of the Bible   Baker
A W Pink

A warm and lucid teaching of the principles. Once again Pink provides an example of how to communicate Truth, though this work is no substitute for Pache and Lightner as far as the serious student is concerned. Paper, £1.90, TB £1.40.

Biblical Numerology Ⓢ   Baker
J J Davis

Dr Davis has given a mine of information in small compass. Highly interesting and will be of great help to preachers, particularly in the solving of problem verses (such as in Kings and Chronicles) where numbers as applied to troops and so forth would seem to be contradictory and unrealistic. 174 pages, paper, £1.90, TB £1.40.

Beginnings in Bible Geography   Moody
H F Vos

Although written for basic home Bible-study groups, this is a fine survey of the Bible lands — their climate and geography. Complete with sketch maps, the book includes Bible-related useful distances and statistics. 126 pages, paper £1.20, TB 95p.

Beginnings in Bible Archaeology   Moody
H F Vos

Also written for those with no previous knowledge, but successful as a small manual for more advanced readers. This book sets the scene and includes details of the main archaeological findings vindicating the Bible. It also has a good bibliography. 112 pages, paper £1.20, TB 95p.

The Old Testament

Chart of the Creation to Abraham   Winona Lake
J C Whitcomb

45p, TB 35p.

Chart of Patriarchs and Judges   Winona Lake
J C Whitcomb

(Early Exodus view) 45p, TB 35p.

Chart of Kings and Prophets   Winona Lake
J C Whitcomb

(Incorporating Thiele chronology). 45p, TB 35p.

Chart of the Babylonian Captivity   Winona Lake
J C Whitcomb

(Two Parts). 90p, TB 70p.

Chart of Between the Testaments   Winona Lake
J L Boyer

45p, TB 35p.
Ⓢ

These charts are inexpensive but of incalculable value. Each gives a
clear picture of its period of Old Testament history. Several
parallel, horizontal "tracks" give the names and dates of
Patriarchs, then Kings, contemporary prophets, neighbouring
Kings (of Assyria etc). At a glance each person may be seen in
relation to all the others. The charts are based on the best
conservative data.

A Survey of Israel's History Ⓢ   **P&I**
Leon Wood

A vital and very readable history which is soundly biblical
(presents the early-exodus view etc). It is up-to-date with its
archaeological evidence, and is furnished with chronological charts
and maps. Wood is essential for tracing out the history of the Old
Testament peoples. 444 pages, cloth, £4.25.

A Chronology of the Hebrew Kings Ⓢ   **Zondervan**
E R Thiele

Dr Thiele's famous work "The Mysterious Numbers of the Hebrew
Kings" is now brilliantly summarised by the author. Not only
deeply instructive but entertaining as the problems of dating are

resolved and the overlapping reigns of the kings are explained. The author is the greatest authority on the subject and should be read by all preachers. There is absolutely no book to match this. 93 pages, paper, £1.90, TB £1.35.

Archaeology and the Old Testament ⑤   Zondervan
Merrill Unger

Out of all the biblical archaeological studies we still select this ageing treatment as the best. First issued 24 years ago it has passed through many printings and revisions. No other book is so readable and Unger is unsurpassed in his marshalling of the arguments when it comes to discussing disputed areas like the Exodus date, or contrasting the Sumerian and biblical flood accounts. Highly recommended. 338 pages, cloth, £5.25, TB £4.25.

Chronological Charts of the Old Testament ⑤   Zondervan
John W Walton

A first class volume of charts which all preachers will value highly. Weights, measures, calendar terms, major archaeological tablets and numerous chronological charts with all the reasoning summarised for the different points of view. Charts include battles of the Judges period, military conflicts of Judah, all the OT dreams and visions, etc, etc. A remarkable and extremely useful work. Outsize format 11" x 8½", 80 pages, paper, £3.10, TB £2.35 (Due January 1979).

An Introduction to the Old Testament ⑤   Eerdmans
E J Young

Prof Young's examination of Old Testament books is still the best available, and is essential to all pastoral studies readers. This great scholar comments in the case of each book on author, contents and purpose. He also discusses and refutes the various ideas of the liberal critics. (The prophetic books are studied from the amillennial standpoint). 432 pages, cloth, £5.50, TB £3.40.

The Theology of the Older Testament ⑤   Zondervan
J Barton Payne

Buried in the jargon and complexities of this big book, is a veritable mass of compressed and valuable matter. The great range of subjects dealt with cannot possibly be summarised here. Dr Payne has provided studies demonstrating the presence of New Testament doctrines in the Old. The Divine attributes, the nature of man, election, redemption, life after death, and morals, are all dealt with. For ten years the author provided notes for Seminary students where (in the study of the theology of the Old Testament) there was no adequate textbook . This work has grown out of these notes. It is not a book which can be read, but a magnificent index makes it a very credible reference work. 554 pages, kivar £4.50, TB £3.40.

Everyday Life in Old Testament Times — Carousel
E W Heaton

Like its New Testament counterpart, this former "Batsford" book so widely used in schools is of little value for spiritual content. But for lively and rich treatment of background matter it is exceptional. The dating material of Exodus/Conquest etc is liberal, but the great quantity of "everyday life" facts make the book valuable. 240 pages, paper, 35p.

The Prophets of Israel — Baker
Leon Wood

This work was the last manuscript completed by Prof Wood before his death. It will appear in 1979 and promises to be a most valuable survey of the writing and non-writing prophets concentrating on the men more than their message. The publishers inform us that Prof Wood covers the prophetic institution — its uniqueness, its dependence upon the Holy Spirit and its relationship to the regular priests and false prophets. The work will be cloth bound with 344 pages, expected price: £6.15, TB £4.75. (To be assessed on RTSRL Review Sheet).

Dead Sea Scrolls and the Bible ⓢ — Baker
C F Pfeiffer

The work shows very clearly the significance of the Scrolls, including the way in which they authenticate the early dating of Old Testament books. Of very great importance. 152 pages, paper £1.85, TB £1.50.

The Epic of Gilgamesh — Penguin
N K Sandars

Useful in conjunction with Dr Unger's "Archaeology and the Old Testament" pages 49-71; and "Survey of Israel's History". 128 pages, paper, 55p.

Mummies, Men and Madness — Baker
J J Davis

An evangelical scholar has given us the fruit of his study and enthusiasm in a 106 page, highly illustrated, lively description of tombs and mummification in Egypt. It is all good Bible background material and the most interesting little book of its kind available. 109 pages, paper, £1.90, TB £1.50.

Between the Testaments Ⓢ　　　　　　　　　　Baker
C F Pfeiffer

A fine and easy history of "The four hundred silent years". Yet these were the years during which much of the prophecy of Daniel (and others) was perfectly fulfilled. A vital study of the last years of OT Order and God's preparation for the New. 132 pages, paper, £2.55, TB £1.95.

A History of Israel　　　　　　　　　　　　　Baker
J J Davis & J C Whitcomb

This volume (due in 1979) will combine the three paperback works — Conquest and Crisis, the Birth of a Kingdom, and Solomon to the Exile (all listed under Old Testament commentaries). It will be clothbound with 568 pages. See comments on individual titles.

The New Testament

New Testament Chronological Chart Ⓢ　　Winona Lake
J L Boyer

Excellent material. Prof Boyer (of Grace Seminary, Indiana) has provided a biblically reliable chart showing the Saviour's ministry sequence; journeys of Paul; dates of NT Books; together with details of contemporary secular governments, etc. 45p, TB 35p.

Chronology of Crucifixion and the Last Week Ⓢ　Winona Lake
J L Boyer

The genius of this chart (with 3-4000 words of explanation on the reverse) is that it manages to describe and compare with amazing simplicity the different views and theories which sound scholars have put forward to explain the events of crucifixion week — "which day?" and so on. Very valuable indeed. 45p, TB 35p.

New Testament Ⓢ　　　　　　　　　　　　　　BT
J Gresham Machen

An Introduction to its Literature and History. "A precious treasure which lay hidden for decades and is now brought to light. It was written by Dr Machen when he taught at Princeton Seminary . . . This is without doubt the finest introduction to the

New Testament." W J Grier — "Evangelical Presbyterian." 386 pages, cloth, £3.00.

Everyday Life in New Testament Times   Carousel
A C Bouquet

Reprinted many times since 1953 and used much in schools. Not commended for its theological content but for the remarkable mass of well presented details of the "homes, clothes, food, finance, commerce, law courts, education and entertainments of the Jews and Gentiles to whom the Gospel was first preached . . ." (Includes even their surgery and dentistry!) Many pictures. (The former Batsford book.) Paper. Last price 40p, reprinting.

Life & Epistles of St Paul Ⓢ   Eerdmans
W J Conybeare & J S Howson

This is the standard work on Paul for evangelicals and is rich with background material. Alongside Goodwin's Harmony this will give as complete a study as is necessary. The portion of the work given to commenting on the Epistles is of relatively little value, but the narrative of the apostle's journeys is superb. See comment on this (and Goodwin) under Commentaries—Acts. 850 pages, cloth, £4.85, TB £4.25.

The Life of St Paul   T & T Clark
J Stalker

"Surpassingly excellent." See reference under Commentaries — Acts. 150 pages, paper, 80p.

A Harmony of the Gospels   P&R
Loraine Boettner

A valuable aid for tracing the order of events and bringing together all the recorded details of any event. The four Gospels are presented as one narrative in the American Standard Version Text. The headings for the events and discourses are very clear and a text index enables the user to trace the location of any Gospel verse. (Also listed under Commentaries). 132 pages, paper, £1.85, TB £1.35.

The Holy Land   Baker
M Avi-Yonah

For advanced readers this work will be appreciated. It is, as the publishers claim, the most reliable and complete treatment of the historical geography of the Holy Land from 536 BC-AD 640. With sketch maps it covers military campaigns and boundary changes, descriptions of city territories, areas and governorships, population details, economic facts, and a brief chapter (with map) on the Roman road system. It is the ultimate work, complete with references. Part of this material gained the author his PhD in London in 1957 and this edition represents a 1977 revision. 249 pages, paper, £2.50, TB £1.85.

Redating the New Testament　　　　　　　　　　　　　　　SCM
John A T Robinson

A leading liberal, author of the notorious "Honest to God" examines the dating of the New Testament books and (while not espousing evangelical doctrine) comes down almost behind our conservative position. This gives a rough time to the flimsy, nonsensical reasoning of other scholars. If it does not embarrass the parrot-lecturers of many divinity and teacher training colleges, they must be beyond all serious intellectual activity. 369 pages, paper, £3.95.

Special Reference Tools

Strongs Exhaustive Concordance　　　　　　　　　　　MacDonald

This is the most famous of the big concordances. This edition is the best, bound in burgundy cloth. It is reprinted from the 1910 edition complete with word numbers and Hebrew and Greek numbered dictionaries enabling those with no knowledge of the original languages to look up the literal meaning of any word. It is an essential tool for preachers. Cloth, £10.95, TB £6.25.

Thayer's Greek-English Lexicon　　　　　　　　　　　　　　Baker
Joseph Thayer

Thayer was Professor of New Testament Criticism at Harvard Divinity School from 1884 until 1901. This big lexicon is coded to Strong's concordance. In other words, the numbers assigned to words in the Strong's references are placed in the margin of Thayer's so that it can also be used by those lacking a knowledge of Greek. Large format. 744 pages, paper, £6.50, TB £4.70.

Davis Dictionary of the Bible　　　　　　　　　　　　　　　P&I
John D Davis

A mature Bible dictionary from the Reformed stable; with contributions from some giants of the faith (B B Warfield etc). Many attractive-looking recent dictionaries are full of poisonous concessions to modernism. This older dictionary is safe and valuable. This new, larger type edition teems with new illustrations and runs to 896 pages. Cloth, £7.95.

Vincent's Word Studies   MacDonald
M R Vincent

Two volumes of excellent New Testament word studies. Paper, the set £6.50, TB £4.50.

Church Order and Government

New Directory of Baptist Churches Ⓢ   **Kregel**
E T Hiscox

This is the only handbook of its kind, reprinted from 1859. A complete rationale of Baptist church organisation boldly subtitled, "An indispensable guide to the conduct and operation of Baptist churches." Discusses forms of government, procedure and grounds for discipline, etc, etc. Follows two-officer system which English Reformed Baptists do not all hold; is closed-table; and is American in places. Is also highly congregational in parts. However it teems with definitions and is complete with resume of Baptist history and the New Hampshire Confession. Every pastor should have this work. 608 pages, cloth, £4.95, TB £3.75.

The Church in God's Program Ⓢ   **Moody**
Robert L Saucy

The title is high-flown and misleading. Actually this is a first-class, straightforward study on the doctrine of the church, and it is all essential material. From the definition of the word 'church' the work passes to its inauguration in the New Testament; its officers, membership terms and organisation; its ministry, worship and ordinances. In all these areas Dr Saucy gives complete proof-texts and scriptural reasoning, together with discussion of the Greek where necessary. Though no work on this subject will command complete agreement and weaknesses occur, this is the best basic tool available to students today. It will prove a mine of stimulation to preachers in preparing to teach these vital themes. 254 pages, paper, £2.25, TB £1.70.

Biblical Separation Defended Ⓢ   **Baker**
Gary Cohen

One of the highest responsibilities of Christian leadership is to *guard* and defend the Truth *and* the Lord's people. For this reason Dr Cohen's book is absolutely essential reading. Written as a reply to the arguments for compromise in evangelism some years ago it is even more important today. The biblical arguments advanced here must be studied and digested. Any pastor not familiar with this kind of material hardly deserves to be taken seriously in these troubled times. 83 pages, paper, £1.00, TB 70p.

Biblical Church Discipline Ⓢ   BT
Daniel Wray

For too long we have heard even Reformed Christians declaring that there are only two grounds of excommunication in the New Testament — immorality and heresy. Such is the widespread shortfall of biblical knowledge about discipline in our day. One should hasten to add that this is not a booklet about excommunication. It is a very able survey of the biblical basis for all discipline. Offences are covered most helpfully but the details of procedure are given scant attention. Clearly the author cannot do everything in such small compass and the work is highly recommended. Booklet, 35p.

Confident Pastoral Leadership Ⓢ   Moody
Howard Sugden and Warren Wiersbe

We may not like the word "confident" but this is a very fine paperback for pastors and church officers. It takes the form of question and answer. The authors arrange scripture quotes for many answers to questions, and give their opinions. Obviously many of the issues are controversial, but the crisp, direct advice given here is usually extremely valuable and often original. Questions range from discerning calls to churches; right down to methods for dealing with difficult members, etc. 160 pages. Kivar, £2.10, TB £1.50.

We Believe — A Guide for Church Fellowships
National Assembly of Strict Baptists

A most useful manual setting out biblical principles (with supporting Scripture texts) for manner and form of worship, preaching, public prayer, hymn singing, church membership and discipline, office bearers (and the appointment of such), baptism, the Lord's Supper, and other matters. 57 page booklet, 25p.

The Downgrade Controversy   Pilgrim
C H Spurgeon

Sombre reading in these days when Spurgeon's predictions have been completely fulfilled, and yet many Evangelicals are determined to continue to compromise. If we involve ourselves in fellowships of churches, are we sure that such fellowships have not just an evangelical basis of faith — but also the machinery to enforce discipline? See entry under Biography and Church History.

Notes

Conspicuous by its absence here is the gigantic work, "The Church of Christ" by James Bannerman. Despite much highly instructive matter, it is fearfully longwinded and in places just too unscriptural to contemplate. James Bannerman was a prophet of the mixed multitude, the font and the theocratic covenant.

The subject of women and office bearing is covered in Dr G W Knight's "New Testament Teaching on the Role Relationship of Men and Women" — see under Pastoral.

Pastoral Ministry–Preaching

The Soul Winner ⓢ   Eerdmans
C H Spurgeon

This series of addresses by Spurgeon is the perfect starting point. Here is counsel, stimulation, sifting and warning. Soul winning is our great work and these exhortations will establish the right mental and emotional attitude for everything else to be read on the subject. Vigorous, deep and vital. 319 pages, paper, £1.70, TB £1.40.

Lectures to my Students ⓢ   Baker
C H Spurgeon

These famous lectures have been read by generations of pastors. Frequently entertaining they nevertheless contain a great mass of help and warning. Some of these spirited passages could have been written directly to our present day pastoral problems. Complete with the well known satirical illustrations of gestures etc. 200 pages. Kivar, £5.10, TB £3.75.

Note

"Counsel for Christian Workers" by Spurgeon (£1.25) is badly titled and is not the same kind of work as those above. It is very basic sermonic exhortation not practical counsel.

Physician of Souls ⓢ   Wakeman
Peter Masters

Subtitled "A guide for preachers and Christian workers to the signs of true conversion, the biblical method of Gospel persuasion, the anatomy of conversion and the counselling of seekers." Includes diagrams illustrating the order of conversion and approaches the problem of the Gospel offer by studying the method and example of the apostles. 144 pages, cloth, £1.60.

Today's Gospel Ⓢ   BT
W Chantry

A vital warning against superficial evangelism which is highly readable. 92 pages, paper, 60p.

An All Round Ministry Ⓢ   BT
C H Spurgeon

Another set of addresses given to ministers. The balance of doctrine and evangelistic action which characterises the Spurgeonic approach is just what is needed today. 396 pages, paper, £1.75.

The Christian Ministry Ⓢ   BT
Charles Bridges

Available once again, this work is of great help to pastors. If old fashioned it has priceless thoughts and advice. The chapter on reading and study has naturally been rendered useless with the passage of time, but its chapters on preaching, and the treatment of categories of unbeliever, cannot be spoken of too highly. 390 pages, cloth, £2.95.

Interpretation of the Scriptures Ⓢ   Baker
A W Pink

We select this as the best and most straightforward work on all the principles to be learned for expounding the different parts of the Word of God. It is by an expository preacher, written from a warm and practical concern to guide other preachers. Schoolmen only complicate this subject, Pink does it justice. Much better than the Berkhof work under the same title. 145 pages. Kivar, £1.90, TB £1.40.

The Ministry of the Word Ⓢ   Baker
W M Taylor

From a noted nineteenth century preacher this offers considerable practical advice to the preacher. It is inclined to exalt the pulpit in a romantic and extreme way. Taylor even advises young ministers to drop everything aside from "pulpit ministrations" in their early years until they develop strength and capacity to add other tasks to their workload! Pioneers will hardly appreciate such counsel. Overall, however, the book is of great value. 318 pages, paper £2.45, TB £1.85.

Thoughts on Preaching ⓢ   BT
J W Alexander

Diffuse, disorganised and repetitive as this work is it contains so much good comment and counsel as to be worth any amount to preachers. If a preacher marked every challenging or profitable sentence the book would be a veritable mass of such marks. It is the kind of work one takes in stages to enjoy and benefit from most. 318 pages, cloth, £2.50.

Pastoral-Counselling

Counselling works have streamed from United States publishers in recent years, including a number of extreme books which would turn Gospel preachers into religious psychiatrists. However it is a simple fact that most of the new generation of counselling works concentrate on various 'techniques', giving practically no real help on the essential matter or substance of counselling. Much of the kind of help which pastoral counsellors will want to have at their fingertips is covered in the range of books listed below. Most are suitable for prescribing to those enquiring about these problems. See also particular subjects. For difficulties on assurance and charismatic problems, see "The Holy Spirit". For intellectual difficulties about the Scriptures, see the first entries under "Apologetics" and so on.

Scripture Reading

Profiting from the Word   BT
A W Pink

The spiritual attitude and approach to Bible study; spiritual counsellors will surely want to prescribe this work widely. 124 pages, paper, 60p.

Guidance

Guidance ⓢ   Wakeman
Peter Masters

This book is intended to help believers generally on the method of obtaining or discerning guidance. Since it is one of the chief subjects which the Lord's people raise with pastors, it is listed here. The chapters deal with the means of seeking guidance, the biblical rules for deciding on leisure pursuits and possessions, the place of ambition and wealth, and how to judge and discern in church issues and evangelistic methods. 91 pages, paper, 90p.

Prayer

The Still Hour   BT
Austin Phelps

A slightly antiquated but still very precious and practical book on prayer to be read and prescribed. (Once enormously popular). Paper, 60p.

Christian Life

Christian Progress Ⓢ   Baker
John Angell James

Starting with the question, "Am I stopping in a mere profession?" this old work is a challenging survey of the nature and the means of progress in the spiritual life. It includes attention to hindrances, motives and encouragements. Do we preach material of this kind? This work has helped tens of thousands of Christians. Today it is a must for preachers and most will want to prescribe it to others. 180 pages, paper, £1.10, TB 95p.

Practical Religion Ⓢ   Baker
J C Ryle

Alongside Christian Progress we must place J C Ryle's great work on the Christian life. How we need these works to challenge the quality of our ministries both for evangelistic worth and direct plainness of speech. Is this our way? An essential book for Christian workers and indeed all believers, though rather long for some. 495 pages, paper, £2.50, TB £1.85.

Sanctification

The Fruit of the Spirit Ⓢ   Zondervan
John W Sanderson

An excellent study of this subject. Along with good definitions and studies of each virtue, the author has provided what must surely be the best modern presentation of spiritual sanctification. He considers weeds and artifical fruit as well as the genuine fruit of the Spirit. He shows how the Spirit of God works to cultivate the fruit by activating or 'watering' conscience, stimulating the effort and actions of believers (not eliminating it) and then strengthening their actions in response. Much original illustration and thought. Recommended for preachers as a model of teaching and also for prescribing. 190 pages, paper, £1.20, TB 90p.

The abridged work of John Owen and the work by Edwin Palmer should be studied for their treatments of sanctification. (See Holy Spirit).

Pastoral — Counselling

29

Bereavement, Heaven, Comfort

Bible on the Life Hereafter Ⓢ   **Baker**
William Hendriksen

This is one of the very best books on all matters relating to death, the 'intermediate state', eternity, the millennium and so on. It is arranged as 3-page-chapter-answers to basic questions. It is fine for giving to believers in need of help. but its arguments and presentation contribute a great lesson to preachers on communication. Not a large book but full of material. (Also listed under Eschatology). 222 pages, paper, £1.20, TB 90p.

A Book of Comfort   **BT**
P B Power

Another comfort-ministry work recently reprinted and rich with exemplary counsel. 100 pages, paper, 60p.

Comfort for Christians   **Baker**
A W Pink

Pink excels in this ministry and should be both studied and prescribed. Paper, £2.60, TB £1.85.

Marriage

The Intimate Life   **James Clarke**
J N Geldenhuys

First issued 25 years ago as a practical handbook for engaged and newly married Christians. Like most books of its kind has a somewhat talk-down tone, but is nevertheless a reliable, brief book for provoking sane and biblical thinking as couples work out their own views before God. It includes facts and tables in connection with the so called 'safe period' approach to family limitation. (It is too old a work to discuss oral contraception). For years pastors have made this book available. 96 pages, cloth, £1.50.

Note

A number of more recent works (together with three announced for imminent publication) on the subject of Christian marriage will be the subject of a comparative review sheet to be issued later.

Parenthood

Dare to Discipline Ⓢ   **Kingsway**
J Dobson

Few would approve all the practical suggestions and "gimmicks" in the book, but it is a commendable and readable challenge to parents with considerable sound biblical material. We list it under "Pastoral" because Christian workers must form early and significant views about the rearing of children, and it is a title pastors may wish to commend to others. 205 pages, paper, 95p.

Notes

Dr Paul D Meier's "Christian Child-Rearing and Personality Development" (Baker, 1977) is available in the UK, but is not recommended here. The author, though undoubtedly a warm, born-again Christian, takes as Gospel truth too many dubious assertions of secular psychiatry. Much of the reasoning in the book is superficial, conclusions tumbling out of half-formed arguments and great fulcrum principles being asserted without the slightest substantiation. Once the gentle chatting and American psycho-jargon (amiable as it is) has been set aside, the author has practically nothing to say on the subject given in the title. "Problems of Adolescence" melt away on a few pages!

Roles of Sexes

NT Teaching on the Role Relationship of Men and Women Baker
G W Knight Ⓢ

To handle this slim work — an expanded essay on the subject — one would expect it to be superficial. But Dr Knight has provided some excellent thinking and reconciles the authority and headship of the man with the equality and mutual giftedness of men and women very ably. Included is treatment of women and office-bearing. Warmly recommended though expensive. 76 pages, paper, £2.15, TB £1.80.

Mental Health

Competent to Counsel Ⓢ   **Baker**
Jay Adams

A spirited presentation of a "confrontation" counselling approach as opposed to Freudian psychiatric counselling. Prof Adams' methods have alarming implications and extremes, and his later books border on the bizarre. Yet for those reading pastoral-studies this book contains much that is important and should be evaluated. 287 pages, paper, £2.60, TB £2.10.

Mental Health: A Christian Approach Ⓢ   **Zondervan-Probe**
Cosgrove and Mallory
For those who desire a brief work explaining the Christian view of mental health as against Freudianism and other worldly systems this is a fine introduction. Paper, £1.95, TB £1.45.

Pastoral–Selected Classics

(Additional great classics of pastoral significance)

Further Soulwinning Works

Being Born Again   Baker
John Angell James

This is Angell James' marvellous work, "The Anxious Inquirer". We feel it is inappropriate to be used evangelistically today (it is long and aimed at nineteenth century middle class formal churchgoers), but its direct style will give an example to Christian counsellors. 212 pages, paper £1.25, TB 90p.

Wilt thou go with this Man?   BT
Brownlow North

If only this had kept its original title, "Yes! or No!". Writing in "The Sword and the Trowel" in 1867, CHS wrote, "The 24th chapter of Genesis . . . is the background for a clear and attractive display of the plan of salvation. Great as Mr North is acknowledged to be as a speaker, we have often heard it said that he is more excellent as a writer; for a certain apparent severity of tone which rather jars in the oral utterance, is, of course, absent from the written appeal." A model of evangelistic use of a passage. 128 pages, paper 50p.

A Call to the Unconverted   Baker
Richard Baxter

Baxter was the great protagonist for Gospel preaching in an age when many Reformed pastors were frightened and inhibited when it came to preaching distinctively evangelistic sermons. That age has caught up with us again and we need a host of Baxters. Here is an example of his work. 135 pages, paper, 90p, TB 60p.

A New Birth   Baker
J C Ryle

Vigorous messages aimed at unbelievers and believers. Are you regenerate? Do you pray? Are you an heir? Are you zealous? These and other question titles are accompanied by a concluding lecture on Whitefield. 322 pages, paper, £1.95, TB £1.30.

Grace Abounding to the Chief of Sinners   Everyman
John Bunyan

The spiritual autobiography of John Bunyan is another essential

Pastoral — Selected Classics

reading item for those who must grapple with troubled seeking souls. Sometimes the work of God in preparing the heart is long, and the sinner stubborn. This will deepen respect and understanding of struggles in conversion. 136 pages, paper, 85p.

Spiritual Walk

The Grace and Duty of being   Baker
Spiritually Minded
John Owen

This classic started life as Owen's private meditations on being spiritually minded. The great Puritan physician of souls gives here a whole course in spiritual anatomy of immense importance. Strongly recommended for further study. 385 pages, paper, £2.20, TB £1.65.

Directions for Daily Communion with God   Baker
Matthew Henry

Rather wordy and for much of the time rather obvious, but including many valuable pieces of counsel. Some exhortations cannot possibly be acted upon by believers in secular life. Waiting upon God as the "constant disposition of our souls" is not even explained! How? To what extent? As a book for prescribing to Christians it is rather over-pious, and this would need to be pointed out or many young believers will run into trouble. 163 pages, paper, £1.00, TB 90p.

Afflictions

The Crook in the Lot   Baker
Thomas Boston

"The Sovereignty and Wisdom of God in the Afflictions of Men Displayed." The ultimate Puritan exposition of the gracious work of God in the "afflicting incidents" in the lives of Christians. Due December 1978. 144 pages, paper, £1.20, TB 90p.

The Eternal State

The Saints' Everlasting Rest   Baker
Richard Baxter

The best part of this famous work is the first three chapters on the nature and excellencies of the Rest. Then chapters on the miseries of those who lose heaven, and the torments of hell will, stir the preacher. The rest of the work is really a general work on the Christian life. 453 pages, paper, £1.70, TB £1.50.

Comfort in Sickness and Death   Baker
R M M'Cheyne

Sweet and gentle discourses on the raising of Lazarus. 94 pages, paper, 80p, TB 55p.

Backsliders

The Rise and Progress of Religion in the Soul   Baker
Philip Doddridge

Philip Doddridge (1702-51) produced this, his best known work, at the age of 46. It became an instrument for the conversion of numerous people, including many 'notables'. Today preachers will appreciate the examples of pastoral counsel to backsliders and relapsers into sin towards the end of the volume. 280 pages, paper, £1.95, TB £1.40.

Saviour's Love

The Redeemer's Tears   Baker
John Howe

A great Puritan piece, written in 1684, reprinted here from an 1846 edition and prefaced with a 53 page "Life of John Howe". Although the title page shows three other works by Howe, only one is actually included in this reprint, "The Redeemer's Tears Wept over Lost Souls" (Luke 24.41-42). This discourse includes material on the sin against the Holy Spirit, the sin unto death and the sense in which God wills the salvation of the lost. Suitable for "further study". 102 pages, paper, £1.50, TB £1.15.

The Martyr Lamb   Baker
F W Krummacher

Not as big or as good as "The Suffering Saviour" but anything on this theme by Krummacher is worth having. The full title is "The Martyr Lamb, or Christ, the Representative of His People in All Ages." 288 pages, paper, £1.60, TB £1.35.

Covenant of Grace

The True Bounds of Christian Freedom   BT
Samuel Bolton

First published in 1645 this outstanding Puritan work expounds the relationship between a Christian and the law. It covers such issues as chastisement, the problem of reconciling duty and freedom, the ethical soundness of performing Christian duties for rewards, and the extent to which Christians are to obey 'men'. Pages 77-109 examine and contrast the arguments of Puritan divines for the three covenant views of Sinai — that it was a dispensation of the Covenant of Grace, that it was a covenant of works, and that it was a subservient third type of covenant. (Bolton renounces the Flavel position in favour of the latter.) This classic passage is most important in the study of Covenant Theology. 224 pages, paper, £1.00.

Heaven Opened   **Baker**
Richard Alleine

"The Riches of God's Covenant Grace." The brother of Joseph Alleine was also a Puritan preacher (1611-81) persecuted under the Great Ejection repressions such as the Five Mile Act. The strident note of this great work overpowers the dated language and carries the reader through some of the finest material ever penned on the Covenant of Grace. (Two chapters of this work were written by Joseph). Due December 1978. 360 pages, paper, £2.45, TB £1.85.

Human Nature

Characters in Pilgrims Progress   **Baker**
A Whyte

Every reading of Pilgrim's Progress reveals more of Bunyan's insight into the different kinds of people we evangelise and counsel. This "commentary" will rekindle appreciation of Pilgrims Progress and assist in turning it to pastoral application. 281 pages, £1.50. TB £1.15.

Note

Bunyan's Holy War is a basic essential for preachers and counsellors being, as it is, the supreme analysis of the soul and its response to the work of grace. Please see comment under Doctrine.

The Pilgrim's Progress is, of course, vital. The Penguin edition uses gently updated punctuation which achieves a lot.

Various Themes

Matthew Henry's Sermon Outlines   **Eerdmans**
Ed S B Quincer

Dr Quincer of Grand Rapids Baptist Seminary has given us a real gem. Instead of reading the theories and opinions of others about the preaching of Matthew Henry we are enabled to sample — in outline — his work directly, and to note the style and construction. 148 pages, paper, £1.50, TB £1.15.

Letters of Samuel Rutherford   BT

Spurgeon's words on Rutherford's letters are frequently quoted, "the nearest thing to inspiration which can be found in all the writings of mere men". 205 pages, paper, 60p,

The Thought of the Evangelical Leaders Ⓢ   BT
Josiah Pratt

"Notes on the Discussion of the Eclectic Society, London, During the Years 1798-1814". During these years John Newton, Charles Simeon, and likeminded men met in 'fraternal' to discuss all kinds of issues. The publication is from the notes made by one of the men. The subjects show up the poverty (and lack of interest in practical issues) of our present day evangelical fraternals. The comments of these men on an amazing variety of issues are of great spiritual importance. In many cases they came to conclusions which a reader will disagree with — but he will at any rate see the best of the "other side" arguments. The work is strongly recommended to pastors and we have to thank the Banner for making it possible for us to sit in on such an illustrious fraternal for some fifteen years-worth of thinking. 535 pages, cloth, £4.50.

Note

William B Sprague's brilliant and comprehensive "Lectures on Revival" (1832) was reprinted by Banner of Truth in 1959 and is certain to be re-issued in 1979 on one side of the Atlantic or the other. Nine lectures covering all aspects of revival are accompanied by 20 letters from eminent preachers contributing valuable comments.

Reviews of reprinted classics of special interest to those engaged in pastoral labours will continue to be made in Review Sheets through 1979 as such reprints are announced.

Apologetics

Alleged Discrepancies of the Bible ⓢ Baker
J W Haley

We welcome this reprint of "old Haley". It is a mine of answers to difficult questions. Here are scores of problems raised by cynics and troubled seekers with fine answers. Do we preachers answer problems like this? Let us learn to. 473 pages, paper, £2.55, TB £1.75.

That Incredible Book the Bible ⓢ Moody
Clifford Wilson

This is a mass market paperback of the station bookstall kind. It is the ideal book to give to interested unbelievers, hospital contacts, sixth-formers, etc. Again, many examples for preachers and much information for young people's leaders. 239 pages, paper, £1.15, TB 85p.

Notes

For other works of biblical vindication see A Chronology of the Hebrew Kings (Thiele) and Biblical Numerology (Davis) under Bible and Old Testament.

Thy Word is Truth BT
E J Young

One of the best works vindicating the Bible by the late Prof Young of Westminster Theological Seminary. Most of the usual arguments for its unique and inspired nature are here, with ample comment. 280 pages, cloth, £2.00.

The Chariots Still Crash Signet
Clifford Wilson

Dr Wilson, an archaeologist, is well known for his best-selling dismissal of Von Daniken. This work goes further and will help youth workers and others to be a good step ahead, and well informed in this area of 'apologetics'. Teems with answers to the questions that teenagers pick up from the unfactual statements of Von Daniken. 182 pages, paper, £1.00.

Rocks, Relics and Biblical Reliability ⓢ Zondervan-Probe
Clifford Wilson

This evangelical Australian scholar is a leading writer in the field of popular apologetics and this book is a very clear and exceptionally interesting treatment of biblical archaeology. Preachers and young people's workers especially will find much material here. 141 pages, paper, £2.40, TB £1.95.

Testing Christianity's Truth Claims Ⓢ   Moody
G R Lewis

A unique crystallisation of the major evangelical apologetic systems. Buswell, Hackett, Clark, Van Til, Carnell, Schaeffer, Pinnock and others are described and assessed. This big Moody book will save buying many others. Complete treatment of modern apologetics. 352 pages, cloth, £6.10, TB £4.50.

Christian Apologetics   Baker
Norman Geisler

A general work dealing with Agnosticism, Rationalism, Fideism, Experientialism, Evidentialism (and historicism), then Deism, Pantheism, Atheism and Theism. 393 pages, cloth, £6.15, TB £4.65.

Mere Christianity Ⓢ   Fontana
C S Lewis

There is a great deal to be learned from this work. C S Lewis marshals numerous arguments to make spiritual things real to needy souls. Throughout, he sets a standard for direct, plain speech. There are major errors and mysterious gaps in C S Lewis's presentation of truth, but the book provides evangelical preachers and counsellors with a challenging example of the art of simple apologetic reasoning. It starts where people are. 189 pages, paper, 75p.

Man's Origin, Man's Destiny Ⓢ   Shaw/Telos
E A Wilder Smith

Out of the vast range of books on creation or evolution this is one of the best from the Christian worker's point of view. It is by a leading scientist of unquestioned international academic integrity. It has much usable information for preachers and teachers (the introduction alone is worth the price), and has a highly original and helpful arrangement of matter and arguments. Paper, £1.80.

The Mythology of Science   P&R
R J Rushdoony

This work is an intellectual "heavy" of considerable value. To more advanced readers it searches out and presents numerous implications of an evolutionary society and is full of significant quotations. 134 pages, paper, £1.85, TB £1.40.

The Dead Sea Scrolls and the Christian Faith   Moody
William La Sor

A good, non-technical treatment of the significance of the Scrolls. Important apologetic material. 251 pages, paper, £2.30, TB £1.70.

Ethical Studies

Ethics, Alternatives and Issues Ⓢ   Zondervan
Norman Geisler

Since 1971 this has been a leading work, reprinted every year. Dr Geisler is Head of the Philosophy of Religion faculty at Trinity Evangelical Divinity School, Deerfield. Part I considers different 'ethical' approaches to life including the antinomianism of philosophers like Kierkegaard, Jean-Paul Sartre, and A J Ayer. Then Generalism, Situationalism, Absolutism and Hierarchicalism are dealt with.

Part II of the work changes style radically to consider ethical issues. First, the current evangelical counselling fancy (particularly in the USA) is covered, namely the exhortation to love oneself. Then Dr Geisler presents the arguments and issues raised (by all sides of the controversy) on the subject of the Christian and War. In similar vein he deals with the Christian's social responsibility; attitude to sex; attitude to birth control, abortion, euthanasia, suicide, capital punishment and the ecology question. Throughout the main attitudes and arguments of evangelicals on these problems are well compared and contrasted. If at times one has to endure the complex style of a philosopher, it is only an intermittent aberration. On the ethical issues Dr Geisler is a good guide. There is an extensive bibliography and an index. 267 pages, cloth, £4.95, TB £3.70.

Eschatology

The Bible on the Life Hereafter Ⓢ   Baker
W Hendriksen

Numerous short chapters. Each deals scripturally with an individual question about the afterlife, "Shall we know one another in Heaven?" "What is the Millennium?" etc. The very best book of its kind. The explanation of Revelation 20 is the briefest and best anywhere. (Also listed under Pastoral). 222 pages, paper, £1.20, TB 90p.

The Momentous Event Ⓢ   BT
W J Grier

Sets out very clearly the Bible's own rules for the handling of prophecy. A lesson in reasoning. Establishes the amillennial position. (Has a fine appendix on Daniel's seventy weeks). 128 pages, paper, 70p.

A Search for Truth — Millennial Studies Ⓢ   Baker
George Murray

The late Prof Murray of Canada has left one of the best treatments of this subject. He seeks by courteous biblical reasoning to lead the reader to amillennial conclusions. He covers problems such as the seventy weeks, the rapture, the resurrection and Revelation 20. 207 pages, paper, £1.85, TB £1.40.

Biblical Studies in Final Things   P&R
W E Cox

If a book ever succeeded in being clear this is surely it. From the "Definition of Terms" section it moves simply and systematically through all the great topics of Final Things. Deals more vigorously with controversial topics than Hendriksen. Both works are complementary and highly recommended — from the amillennial point of view. 226 pages, paper, £1.60, TB £1.20.

Israel in Prophecy Ⓢ   Baker
William Hendriksen

A very important book which shows how the Jews should be regarded. Sane and biblical chapters disperse the confusing clouds of alleged Divine favouritism. First rate perspective, together with sound help on distinguishing between literal and figurative prophecies. 63 pages, paper, £1.25, TB 85p.

Backgrounds to Dispensationalism   Baker
Clarence Bass

Dr Bass here surveys the distinguishing features of dispensationalism before examining in detail its origin in the teaching of Irving and Darby. In a thorough piece of scholarly writing he focusses on Darby as a man, his doctrine of the church and his eschatological views. The conclusions sound a clear warning on the dangers of dispensationalism. In the light of the evidence produced (which shows Darby to have been capable of great arrogance and vindictiveness) Dr Bass is unfailingly courteous and gentle in his comments and handling of the man. The bibliography is very extensive. 184 pages, paper, £2.25, TB £1.85.

Eschatology

An Examination of Dispensationalism   P&R
W E Cox

The comparatively modern exegetical hocus-pocus of dispensationalism is deservedly exposed here. The rise and teaching of dispensationalism is plainly described and vigorously countered. Brief, crisp and clear. Some elements of Darbyism are misunderstood by the author, but that should not weaken the essential argument of the book. 61 pages, paper, 95p, TB 65p.

Amillennialism Today   P&R
W E Cox

This short work gives the author of "Biblical Studies in Final Things" an opportunity to deal more positively and enthusiastically with the amillennialist position. 143 pages, paper, £1.60, TB £1.20.

What, Where, When is the Millennium?   Baker
R B Jones

From the amillennial point of view this is very well presented, fresh and not too long. 144 pages, paper, £1.90, TB £1.40.

The Doctrine of Eternal Punishment   P&R
H Buis

Another subject too rarely covered. (This was the doctrine at the hub of the Baptist Downgrade Controversy of the 1880s). This book is brief and clear, surveying the teaching of the Scriptures and of the Church through history. The passage on those dying in infancy could be (biblically) much more optimistic but, overall, vital material is exceedingly well presented. 148 pages, paper, £1.60, TB £1.20.

More than Conquerors   Baker
William Hendriksen

This is such an important presentation of the amillennial interpretation of the Book of Revelation that it is listed here. Please refer to Commentaries, Revelation.

Note

The section entitled "The Last Things" in Berkhof's "Systematic Theology" is the most concise and Scripture-based presentation of the amillennial position to be had. His method of tracing the second-coming teaching of Christ Himself, then of the apostle Paul, to demonstrate their "ignorance" of premillennial events, is very powerful. So we enthusiastically direct readers to that section as it is better than many of the specialised books on the subject.

Church History and Biography

The Pilgrim Church Ⓢ   **P&I**
E H Broadbent

Books written to prove a point always read very much better than
academic history books. The writer's point is that particular
blessing has always attended a serious attempt (however
incomplete) to return to the pattern church of Scripture. With
readable histories at a premium this is strongly recommended. 421
pages, paper, £1.40.

A Short History of the Early Church Ⓢ   **Eerdmans**
H R Boer

This span of the first centuries is crystal clear and will enable the
reader to discern the cause and course of many errors and false
traditions, as well as seeing the true church in action. Dr Boer is an
old hand at making church history both exciting and meaningful.
There is no other brief history quite like this one. 184 pages,
paper, £1.80, TB £1.50

Early Christian Writings   **Penguin**

An inexpensive selection of early writers which will form a very
useful companion to Boer and Broadbent. 237 pages, paper, 90p.

The Early Christian Fathers   **Oxford**
Ed H Bettenson

This selection from the writings of the Early Christian Fathers
helpfully arranges excerpts under doctrinal headings where
possible. So one may turn to a sample of Clement, Irenaeus,
Tertullian etc under 'Atonement' or 'Sacraments' and so on. It is
Bettenson's own modern translation. 318 pages, paper; reprinting
for 1979, new price not announced.

Here I Stand Ⓢ   **Mentor**
R H Bainton

1483-1546. This is *the* biography of Luther. While Bainton does
not stand quite where Luther stood, he is a sympathetic historian
and a great writer. There is no better insight (in print) into
Luther's Reformation labours. 336 pages, paper, £1.50.

Martin Luther   **Arnold**
E G Rupp & R Drewery

1483-1546. Prepared for the Open University, this is an anthology

Church History & Biography

of Luther's own writings and opinions in modern English. The pieces selected afford an opportunity of appreciating first hand Luther's words and work in key situations through his life. 179 pages, paper, £1.95.

The Life and Times of Martin Luther   Moody
J H Merle d'Aubigne

1483-1546. The new Wycliffe edition in large format and large print. Reset from the longer history of the Reformation by the author. (This appears in the Baker volume referred to below.) Those who hve enjoyed d'Aubigne on The Reformation in England will want this fine volume. Expected December 1978, paper, £5.10, TB £3.75.

Calvin Ⓢ   James Clarke
E Stickelberger

1509-64. Easily the most exciting biography of Calvin by a great man of letters. Reads like a novel. Calvin's heroic early years are stirring material. One identifies to the point of wanting to call out to Calvin to stop when he tangles with politics in Geneva. 173 pages, cloth, £3.15.

John Calvin   Lion
T H L Parker

1509-64. This work is as orderly and dour as the Stickelberger biography is explosive and moving. While being unnecessarily dry, it is full of information not available elsewhere. 217 pages, paper, £1.95.

The Reformation in England Ⓢ   BT
J H Merle d'Aubigne

The great Genevan professor's work is another which reads like a novel. These volumes begin the story back in the early centuries of the witness in Britain and cover the Reformation period as only a converted scholar can. We rate this as essential reading for Christian workers. (The modern treatment by Prof Dickens is a most reassuring confirmation of the integrity of the nineteenth century Genevan scholar's work). Complete with many excellent illustrations. Cloth, 2 vols, each £4.50.

History of the Reformation   Baker
J H Merle d'Aubigne

This is a one-vol, very small print edition of the work which includes the original portions of the work covering Germany, Switzerland and France. Unfortunately it ends half way through the English Reformation — exactly where Vol I of the Banner of Truth work ends. It is therefore only of use to readers who particularly require the sections on countries referred to. This is the edition Evangelical Press take here. At the high price asked it is a great shame that the volume should be seriously incomplete. It is most important to have the second half of the English Reformation and therefore the large, modern print of the superior Banner volumes are essential. (The long portion on Luther's life is best read in the new large-print Moody work.) Cloth, £9.60, TB £6.95.

Foxe's Christian Martyrs Ⓢ   **Moody**
John Foxe

"The blood of the martyrs is the seed of the church." What a cloud of witnesses! No one in Christian service dare leave out a feelingful reading of Foxe. To read Foxe will mean more courage, more sacrifice and much less self pity in the Lord's service. (And what can present-day ecumenical compromisers possibly have in common with such martyrs.) The Moody edition is by far the nicest available. 590 pages, cloth, £5.00, TB £3.75.

Anabaptist Story Ⓢ   **Eerdmans**
W R Estep

Professor Estep's revised work is vital. The Anabaptists have been maligned and dismissed for too long. In our own land Baptists were very numerous among the Lollards, and it is now known that 80% of those executed by Mary were Baptists. This complete history is exceedingly moving and challenging. 250 pages, paper, £2.40, TB £1.95.

The English Reformation Ⓢ   **Everyman**
A G Dickens

The very best on the Reformation from a secular source. Prof Dickens writes as a historian, but one who is sympathetic and faithful to facts. For advanced readers the references are an essential introduction to the key sources and modern works for each stage of the Reformation. 511 pages, paper, £1.25.

The Reformation   **Baker**
H J Hillerbrand

Hillerbrand has assembled primary source material here. We are not reading about the Reformers, but we are reading modern translations of the comments, letters, statements and diary excerpts of the Reformers themselves (and other eye-witnesses) about the great events of the Reformation. A very important

addition to the Reformation section of our shelves. 498 pages of
fascination, with many surprises. 498 pages, paper, £4.30, TB
£3.30.

The Reformation . . . to the Accession of Elizabeth I   **Arnold**
A G Dickens & Dorothy Carr

A selection of letters, statements etc from the pens of the
personalities of the Reformation. Includes letters of Bilney, Barnes
Frith — State Papers etc etc. Of absorbing interest to students of
the Reformation. Another volume is coming on the Elizabethan
Settlement. 167 pages, paper, £2.50.

Autobiography of Richard Baxter   **Dent**

(1615-91) From his boyhood and conversion Baxter takes us
through his work, persecution, and wrangles with John Owen and
others. This great classic is a window on the great preacher of the
"middle way" and his turbulent times. 314 pages (with index),
paper, £1.50.

God's Statesman — The Life and Work of John Owen **Paternoster**
Peter Toon

(1616-83) A solid modern work. The author is thoroughly at
home in the literature of this period. Scholarly rather than
popular in style. 200 pages, cloth, £4.20.

Life of John Bunyan Ⓢ   **Baker**
John Bunyan

(1628-88) Autobiographical statements are carefully selected from
the range of Bunyan's works, and linked together with editorial
notes of dates and events. The result forms a fine popular life of
Bunyan. 160 pages, paper, 95p, TB 75p.

Isaac Watts Remembered Ⓢ   **GSBT**
D G Fountain

(1674-1748) Here is an insight into the whole period and situation
in which the sweet psalmist of nonconformity lived and
ministered. It is full of information, and particularly important as
the period receives scant attention in church history works. 111
pages, paper £1.50.

The Axminster Ecclesiastica   **Gospel Tidings**
Ed: K W H Howard

(1660-98) The value of a record written at the time of the affairs
of a congregational church at Axminster from 1660 to 1698 is far
greater than might at first be apparent. Such a description of the

government, spirituality and concerns of an independent church after the Restoration is unique. This shortened and tastefully edited edition allows us to see the life of the Axminster congregation and that of neighbouring fellowships also; the terrible effects of their involvement in the Monmouth rebellion; the persecutions, and their strength and blessings. It is a moving chronicle which will make a deep impression on the reader and communicate a real sense of history. 280 pages with illustrations, cloth, £3.80.

George Whitefield Ⓢ   BT
Arnold Dallimore

(1714-70) The life of Whitefield is of enormous importance to preachers. So is the whole period of the awakening which began in 1739. Dr Dallimore has devoted over 20 years to this work. Take careful note of the blood, sweat and tears which is the cost of such human instrumentality. Too many people today claim Whitefield as their prophet who know nothing of his sacrificial, holy activism and relentless evangelism. 598 pages, Vol I only £4.50.

The Burning Heart Ⓢ   Paternoster
A Skevington Wood

(1703-91) With Wesley biographies in short supply we are glad to have this one. The author's own comments and conclusions are frequently in contradiction with the evidence he presents. He is nothing like as good a thinker as he is an historical researcher. But for the facts, we value this book. 302 pages, paper, £2.40.

The Journal of John Wesley Ⓢ   Moody

Edited portions of the Journal from 1735 to 1790. Over 400 pages with a biographical sketch and an account of Wesley's last hours. The Journal takes us through the mob violence of the revival years and is informative and challenging. It makes particularly interesting reading in the wake of Dallimore. 419 pages. Kivar, £3.10, TB £2.25

Note

"John Wesley, His Life and Theology" by Robert Tuttle, newly issued by Zondervan, is hardly a sufficient biography. Most of the book is spent on getting Wesley to Bristol in 1739 leaving only a few pages for his life's work. The work is mostly written in the first person as though Wesley himself were the author. This novel and alarming device is, in the opinion of this reviewer, a complete disaster. The author's style cannot possibly represent the personality (let alone the literary capability) of the great John

Church History & Biography

Wesley. Injury must be done to the historical process. Furthermore the author is obliged to present everything from Wesley's point of view. Needless to say the less savoury aspects of Wesley's conduct (such as the seizing of Whitefield's Kingswood School and his failure to stand up to his father over the inhuman treatment of poor Hetty) must be glossed over or whitewashed by the preposterous first-person technique. This really is just not a serious contribution.

The Life of John Newton — Baker
Richard Cecil

(1725-1807) A reprint of his letters to Thomas Hawies relating his life, conversion and subsequent experience up to 1763 with a continuation to his death by Richard Cecil. This is the unedited version of the work which is published in slightly shortened form by Moody under the title, "Out of the Depths". 244 pages, paper, £1.80, TB £1.40.

Christian Leaders of the 18th Century ⓢ — BT
J C Ryle

Banner have now issued Ryle's portraits of 18th century preachers without omission. All eleven were greatly admired by Ryle and his flowing, vigorous style is seen here at its best. The reading of this quality paperback is essential. 432 pages, paper, £1.75.

Note

A resurgence of revival chronicles is anticipated during 1979.
(To be covered by forthcoming RTSRL Review Sheets).

The Great Awakening ⓢ — BT
Joseph Tracy

In 1841 this writer gathered the source material of the New England awakening of 1740 to produce this account. He provides a marvellous chronicle with much information on Whitefield and Jonathan Edwards, and follows the revival through to its decline, "warts and all". 433 pages, cloth, £3.00.

Life of David Brainerd — Baker
Edited by Jonathan Edwards

(1718-47)"Chiefly extracted from his diary" by Edwards, the life of this truly selfless missionary continues to be a rebuke, a challenge and an inspiration to labourers in the Lord's vineyard. (This is also in Vol 2 of The Works of Jonathan Edwards; BT.) 360 pages, paper, £2.25, TB £1.60.

To the Golden Shore — Adoniram Judson Ⓢ   Zondervan
Courtney Anderson

(1788-1850) A moving and detailed life of the first American overseas missionary who left his homeland a Congregationalist and set foot in Rangoon, Burma, a Baptist. What an account of sacrificial pioneering in seemingly impossible circumstances this is! The work also gives a valuable insight into the worship of late 18th century American Congregationalism. How much we need this pioneering faith in the towns and villages of Britain today. 530 pages, paper, £2.45, TB £1.90. (New US Edn).

The Early Years (Vol I) Ⓢ   BT
The Full Harvest (Vol II)
C H Spurgeon

(1834-92) In the work of this mighty man of God we see another perfect combination of doctrinal Calvinism and aggressive, activistic evangelism. C H Spurgeon was a man of tremendous feeling; a great labourer; an uncompromising separatist; and the most applicatory preacher of his day. Again, he is a man with countless disciples but few imitators. What volumes these are! Two volumes, cloth, £4.00 each.

The Downgrade Controversy Ⓢ   Pilgrim
C H Spurgeon

Pilgrim Publications have here reprinted all Spurgeon's Sword and Trowel editorials, fragments and notes on this controversy together with the relevant chapter assembled by Mrs Spurgeon and J W Harrald for the Autobiography. Most important source material. 100 pages, paper, £2.35, TB £1.45.

Love Them In (D L Moody) Ⓢ   Moody
S N Gundry

(1837-99) Dr Gundry's treatment of Moody reveals his total familiarity as a scholar with all the Moody literature. This work is firstly highly enjoyable. Secondly, it shows Moody as a deeper man theologically than is often appreciated. Thirdly, it contains exceptionally good thumbnail treatments of other personalities of American revivalism — Finney, etc — with most discerning critiques. Highly recommended. 252 pages, cloth, £4.85, TB £3.50.

George Muller: Delighted in God   H&S
Roger Steer

This modern biography is a great improvement on A T Pierson and besides giving a clear life of George Muller, yields a good picture of

Church History & Biography

emerging Brethrenism. 351 pages, cloth, £4.95.

The Korean Pentecost   BT
W N Blair & B F Hunt

"The Korean Pentecost and the Sufferings Which Followed" must be one of the most remarkable records of missionary experience penned. The authors' ministries in Korea (father and son-in-law) covered 76 years, years which saw wonderful revival and terrible persecution. 162 pages, paper, 70p.

Note

F F Bruce's "The Spreading Flame" is not recommended due to the persistent blurring of the line between Evangelical and Catholic figures in early church history.

General Works

Men of Destiny   Wakeman
Peter Masters

In the course of this selection of brief biographies (which will afford much illustrative material for preachers and teachers) the lives of Alfred the Great and Martin Luther are particularly relevant for church history readers. Alfred is not sufficiently dealt with elsewhere (in print) and Bainton's biography is weak on Luther's conversion, which is the sole substance of the article in this book. 144 pages, cloth, £1.95.

Men of Purpose   Wakeman
Peter Masters

This collection of great Christian lives (stressing conversions) includes the born-again fathers of modern science, with earlier worthies such as non-conformist Daniel Defoe; hymnwriters James Montgomery and Philip Bliss; and the converted brewer preacher Fred Charrington. Some of these remarkable lives are not covered elsewhere, and all will increase the Christian Worker's arsenal of testimony illustration. 143 pages, cloth, £1.75.

Documents of the Christian Church   Oxford
Ed H Bettenson

Nearly 35 years of publication have made this selection of quotations from church historical sources an immoveable part of the scene. Early Fathers, popes, reformers, persecuting Acts of Parliament — all are freely plundered to bring source material direct to the student. (Reprinting early 1979). 362 pages, paper, £2.25.

Who's Who in Church History   Baker
W P Barker

Brief but very useful, this book has thumbnail descriptions of
1500 names. Invaluable, but far from perfect on account of many
omissions. A hardback since 1969 now available in this form. 319
pages, paper, £1.90, TB £1.40.

Cult Studies

Gist of Cults Ⓢ   Eerdmans
J K Van Baalen

A very useful short work on the cults. Concisely summarised
information. 71 pages, paper 75p, TB 65p.

The Chaos of Cults   P&I
J K VanBaalen

A large study of all the main cults, including biographical details
of their founders; accounts of their commencement; details of
their teachings; and the biblical way to refute them. 410 pages.
Reprinting.

The Four Major Cults   Paternoster
A A Hoekema

An alternative volume concentrating on four cults. The history
and doctrines of Mormons, Christian Scientists, Seventh Day
Adventists and Jehovah's Witnesses, together with chapters on the
distinctive features of a cult and the way to approach the cultist.
464 pages, paper, £2.80.

The Teachings of . . . series Ⓢ   Baker
John H Gestner

A comparison of the tenets of different cults with evangelical
Christian doctrine. There are individual booklets for the following
— Seventh Day Adventism, Jehovah's Witnesses, Mormonism,
Christian Science. Each one gives a background to the movement,
details of founding personalities and doctrine. All are very well
done by Prof Gestner of Pittsburg Theological Seminary. 80p
each, TB 60p each.

A Christian Introduction to Religions of the World Ⓢ   Baker
J G Vos

A much used work which goes beyond the cults to the other major religions. Because of the multi-racial society we are now much more in need of help in this area than that of cults. To study the chief characteristics of religions of human manufacture also provides strong apologetic material in favour of the one 'revealed' religion. 98 pages, paper, £1.25, TB 90p.

A Christian's Response to Islam   P&R
W E Miller

A most important work standing practically alone. 178 pages, paper, £2.15, TB £1.65.

The Plain Truth about Armstrongism   Baker
Roger Chambers

Nothing could be clearer than this investigation of Armstrongism from an American pastor. 146 pages, paper, 75p, TB 60p.

We Left Jehovah's Witnesses   Baker
E C Gruss

Personal testimonies by six couples — some from high positions on the American side of the movement. Dr Gruss is a professor at Los Angeles Baptist College. 169 pages, paper, £1.80, TB £1.40.

Is Mormonism Christian?   Moody
G H Fraser

Very helpful indeed, by an expert, yet written in a clear style. 192 pages, paper, £1.35, TB 95p.

Contemporary Counterfeits   Baker
John J Davis

Those impressed by the fine commentaries of Dr Davis may write for this work under the impression it is a serious treatment of the theme. While a useful booklet for young believers who may need the elementary advice given, it is only a 43 page booklet giving four pages to each "counterfeit" dealt with — astrology, tea-leaves, etc. 43 pages, paper, 80p, TB 60p.

Freud (Modern Thinkers Series)   P&R
R J Rushdoony

Rushdoony never fails to be provocative and full of matter. In our Freud-ridden culture we need to be able to demonstrate to men what their godless society is built on. But we shall have to learn a jargon-free, clear style of communication which our author has not been able to achieve. 69 pages, paper, 95p, TB 70p.

Cult Studies

Appendix– Bible Surveys

A Comparative Review

A number of survey works are available, including some that are weak and unsound (such as "The Lion Handbook to the Bible"). The difficulty with all such surveys is to determine who they are suited for. Young Christians require one kind of work; those preparing children's meetings and youth classes require another; and the requirements of preachers are different again. The trouble is that most surveys claim to be useful for all.

Two survey works which are thoroughly Evangelical and reliable are Dr William Hendriksen's "Survey of the Bible" (Evangelical Press) and Dr Irving L Jensen's "Jensen's Survey of the Old Testament" (Moody Press). As far as preachers and Christian workers are concerned, the compiler's choice is rather decidedly in favour of the Jensen work, in spite of the fact that it covers only the Old Testament.

The highly respected Reformed commentator Dr Hendriksen has, in the case of his survey, constructed a rather difficult-to-use volume (contrasting sharply with his magnificent commentary style). Beginning with useful chapters on Bible facts and rules of interpretation, Dr Hendriksen gives 116 pages to a bird's-eye-view summary of Bible history. This is a pity because it is not the kind of presentation to which one can refer very easily, and it compresses the more orthodox survey of each book of the Bible into 234 remaining pages. The surveys are good but much too brief to be useful to Christian workers.

"Jensen's Survey of the Old Testament" is in a slightly bigger format with thick paper and a much more acceptable presentation. Its treatment of Bible dates (and similar complexities) is better because Dr Jensen uses large, clear charts. Not counting introductory articles and indices this book gives 410 pages to an orthodox survey of each book of the Old Testament. Each is discussed as regards background, theme, content, doctrines, and APPLICATIONS. (These sections are extremely good.) There are charts and maps, and for each book there is a long, detailed bibliography (the absence of any worthwhile bibliography in Dr Hendriksen's survey is a serious deficiency). Dr Jensen also gives page references to Evangelical reference works where the best information is to be found. Dr Jensen is a decided premillennialist, but there is little eschatological treatment in the book with the exception of a few pages with charts in the Daniel section.

A comparison of the two books in their treatment of Proverbs and Job, reveals the following:—

Dr Hendriksen: Proverbs = 1½ pages, being a division of the book into categories. Job = 7 pages, most of which is made up of lengthy quotations from the book of Job. The analysis of the book is exceedingly simple. One cannot feel that preachers would derive anything from such brief passages.

Dr Jensen: Proverbs = 12 pages of condensed information with charts, prominent themes, and 1½ pages of application with advice on interpretation, and a bibliography. Job = 19 pages under the title, "Knowing God Better Through Adversity" and with the usual Jensen content including 1½ pages of applications and a bibliography.

It must in fairness be admitted that Dr Hendriksen's book covers the whole Bible, but the compiler's feeling is that most users of these Surveys require them most (and refer to them most) for Old Testament books. The value of Jensen is, therefore, far greater. It is a book which one can imagine being used much by teachers and also by preachers. The applications section alone make the work worth every penny of its price. (Dr Irving Jensen is Professor of Bible at Bryan College, Dayton.)

"Survey of the Bible" by William Hendriksen (EP) 497 pages, cloth, costs £5.95. "Jensen's Survey of the Old Testament" by Irving L Jensen (Moody) is better value for a larger format work, 488 pages, cloth, £5.00,TB £4.25.

Historical Survey of the Old Testament   Baker
Eugene Merrill

A very good general survey of Old Testament history. The author has an exceptional ability to make a serious study readable and enjoyable, but the great strength of this work is its unswerving allegiance to conservative scholarship. In controversial areas the arguments on all sides are well presented and liberal errors (together with neo-evangelical compromise) exposed. Much recent archaeological (and linguistic) information is included. A valuable aid to clearing up the foggy patches in one's grasp of biblical history. 343 pages, paper, £3.10, TB £2.30.

A Select Bibliography of Evangelical Commentaries

The main objective in selecting commentaries has been to provide material which is of most value to preachers and teachers. Some technical works are included, but the works which offer the richest spiritual and practical application are the favourites.

The emphasis on older commentaries and reprinted classics will be very apparent. The reasons are simple. With a few notable exceptions, modern 'Evangelical' commentators seem quite unable to include applicatory and experimental material in their work. Modern commentators commence with long introductions discussing authorship, date, etc (introductions in which the infidel theories of unbelieving theologians are taken far too seriously). They proceed to expound the Scriptures purely by discussion of the original language — "The Hebrew indicates such and such," or "the force of the Greek is thus and thus." Obviously this is an important part of a commentator's work, and such word studies are to be used, but we have come to the stage where there is such duplication and multiplication of the same explanations and comments that it is just pointless issuing new commentaries in this style. Are not the authors aware that they are contributing nothing new?

An added defect with the current stream of modern Evangelical commentaries is the fact that they barely ever go *beyond* technical discussion of the words in the original. And when they do, the comment is so elementary as to be worthless. The standard of spiritual application is so poor; the level of suggestion to preachers so low; the citing of Barclay, C H Dodd, and a host of positively non-evangelical academics so frequent, that one is bound to react back to the fervent, rich, spiritual and experimental style of the past. Whether judged intellectually or spiritually they are far superior works. However, notable exceptions will be found in this list — a cluster of worthy, spiritual 'moderns' from both sides of the Atlantic. May there be many more.

Tyndale—IVP commentaries and Eerdmans New International Commentary series are not (with two exceptions) included in this selection, representing as they do a very poor standard of work measured by experimental and suggestive requirements. There is little in them which the average preacher could not write himself with minimal effort. The Tyndale commentaries are far too brief to be useful, include many serious concessions to liberal views, and are characterised by very obvious comment, particularly in the New Testament books. The NIC series aims higher but generally fits the complaints made earlier against 'moderns'.

Just a word of caution is fitting concerning some of the new, small reprint publishers appearing in the USA. Considerable Reformed sympathy is evident, but so far some very mixed selections have been issued. Because some first-rate commentaries are being reprinted by these friends, preachers should not assume that everything is useful, or even sound. (One such house is overfond of the old "Expositors Bible" volumes. Some of these are very good Evangelical commentaries. Others are painfully liberal).

We are being assailed by reprints of anglo-catholic and liberal authors — highly technical and often highly unspiritual. These will take a heavy toll on many an unwary preacher's resources. So it is important to check the usefulness of each author, and not to trust a publisher's name.

A question frequently asked is — may Calvin's Old Testament commentaries still be obtained? Eerdmans (USA) had the entire set in print for many years, but they have now gone out of print. An Old Testament set was recently issued (in not very nice type) by the ill-fated "APA" imprint (USA). They are all the old translation of Calvin's commentaries, whereas the New Testament volumes published by St Andrews Press, Edinburgh are the new Torrance translation. Why cannot some of the USA publishers who do so well making photo-litho books from classics, (thus saving all royalties and typesetting) commission a new translation of Calvin's Old Testament commentaries? They could do something like this instead of paying royalties and typesetting for some of the rather pointless large modern commentaries being issued. The fact is that Old Testament Calvins are not now available. The Banner of Truth still publish "Genesis" and used to have "Daniel" also, but the latter has gone out of print.

May the Lord help us to keep even the best commentaries in second place to the study and application of the innerrant Word itself.

Commentaries:
Whole Bible & Entire Old Testament

Lange's Commentary On The Holy Scriptures   Zondervan
J P Lange

"I greatly prize the series produced under the presidency of Mr Lange. The volumes differ in excellence, yet none could be spared. We have nothing equal to them as a series." (Spurgeon) This great commentary continues in the Zondervan edition. Some of the volumes are among the finest on a particular book of the Bible — the 'Job' volume being an example. Cloth, 12 volumes, £124.00 the set, TB £85.00.

Matthew Henry's Commentary on the Whole Bible   MacDonald

Matthew Henry, however antiquated and even quaint in places, is the prince of application. Here is an unflagging emphasis on applying the Word in an experimental way to the real problems and needs of the soul. Here we can learn such skills from a master of his craft. This edition is unabridged, of high quality, being heavily bound with gold blocking title and spine decoration. Cloth, 6 volumes, £34.00, TB £22.00.

A Commentary on the Holy Bible   BT
Matthew Poole

Despite its age, this work still stands out for the brilliant and clear explanations offered in such brief, verse by verse comments. There is little specific application, but as an explanatory kind of commentary, it evades no problem. The modern offerings, such as the IVP one-volume commentary, are nowhere near the usefulness and spiritual style of these old works. One wonders why people bother with them. Poole could honestly say, "We have not willingly baulked any obvious difficulty." Three large volumes: Gen-Job/Psalms-Mal/N.T. Cloth, over 1000 pages each, £6 each.

Commentary on the Whole Bible   Zondervan
Jamieson, Fausset & Brown

This one-volume edition is a recently reset issue from Zondervan. The original full length work incorporated comment from all the major exegetes. The compilers (leading nineteenth century evangelical preachers and scholars) added their own thoughts to produce one of the best commentaries ever. This shortened edition is probably the finest one-volume commentary available. 1590 pages, cloth, £10.05, TB £8.95.

Keil & Delitzsch Old Testament Commentary   Eerdmans

For more than one hundred years, this series of commentaries has remained the foremost authority for the elucidation of the text. They are not generally suggestive or experimental, indeed they are often dry in style, and ideally require some knowledge of Hebrew as the Hebrew text is discussed a great deal. But they are packed with painstaking, detailed exegesis, representing the zenith of German evangelical scholarship. Especially in the case of books where so much hangs on an understanding of the words, e.g. Job, Proverbs, Ecclesiastes, to mention only three, there is no richer, fuller source of information, Ten volumes, cloth. The set £57.75, TB £48 (special price £40 pastors). Reprint due March, 1979.

Christology of the Old Testament   Kregel
E W Hengstenberg

A half-length and highly successful abridgement of the acclaimed (but formidable) work. The original work wasted much print repudiating dead and forgotten unbelieving scholars. This abridgement clips out most of those portions, preserving all the vital arguments of Hengstenberg as he traces the Messianic passages through the Old Testament. There is treatment of all such passages in Genesis and the Psalms; but the attention given to such books as Isaiah, Jeremiah and Zechariah is so extensive as to constitute almost three complete separate commentaries. Then Ezekiel and Daniel (with a long section on the seventy weeks) and the remaining minor prophets are all covered. This, the best-known work of Hengstenberg, is a foundation stone in the preacher's library (and this Thomas Arnold abridgement of 1847 is the most usable edition available). 700 pages, cloth, £6.15, TB £4.75.

Preaching from the Types and Metaphors of the Bible   Kregel
Benjamin Keach

It is good to have Keach back in print. Persecuted for the faith, he was the second pastor of what is now the Metropolitan Tabernacle (Spurgeons) and was one of the compilers of the 1689 Baptist

Confession. He compiled the first Baptist hymn-book and introduced hymn-singing as we know it into English worship. This book contains many quaint things, but it is packed with rich suggestion for preachers. Those who can catch (and update) the spirit of this great preacher will derive much stimulation. Formerly "Tropologia: A Key to Open Scripture Metaphors, together with Types of the Old Testament." This reprint is from the 1855 revision. 1007 pages, cloth, £8.00, TB £6.25.

Jensen's Survey of the Old Testament   Moody
Irving L Jensen

An excellent survey giving considerable information on each book; with many charts and a long section on "Applications" in each case. While aimed (like most of such surveys) at the general reader, this is one which really will be used by teachers, Bible class leaders and preachers also. There is a good, credible bibliography for every Old Testament book. Premillennial in the treatment of Daniel — but eschatological content generally minimal. We think this is much better than Dr Hendriksen's survey. See extended comparison in appendix. 488 pages, cloth, £5.00, TB £4.25.

Note

We definitely advise against the IVP New Bible Commentary with its many concessions to liberalism and its painfully light standard of comment. Clearly there are exceptions such as E J Young on Daniel (but it is far better to have the complete book by Prof Young). Generally, however, it will be found fruitless for devotional use due to its lack of spiritual application, and grossly inadequate (even unsound in parts) for technical use by teachers.

If it can be found second-hand the famous Hall's Contemplations will give preachers a great deal of highly original reflection. The full title is "Contemplation on the Historical Passages of the Old and New Testament" by Rt Rev Joseph Hall DD. Copies of the last century SPCK reprints still abound. The work comes in three small volumes, is written in an irresistible 'conversational' style, and teems with observations which are full of meaning and stimulation for a preacher, but just not seen anywhere else. Half-an-hour with Hall makes most commentaries seem just commonplace.

See Old and New Testament sections of Reading List for Introductions for each Testament.

Genesis

Genesis
Robert S Candlish
Kregel

The work is applied and full of suggestions for preachers. One of the very few OT commentaries which will help in the preparation of EVANGELISTIC addresses. Kregel have re-issued the 2 volume Black edition in one fine volume at our request. Spurgeon's favourite Genesis commentary will doubtless be the immediate favourite of many preachers today. Expected April 1979, cloth, about £6.00.

Genesis
John Calvin
BT

A great example of Calvin's genius. The more one uses Calvin the more one appreciates him. He never gets tied down with individual verses in spite of being the most thorough of commentators. He always leads one to the whole meaning of a passage or an event revealing a whole drift of argument. Because of this style, more than any other commentator, he helps the preacher to search out the overall application which must be communicated.   523 pages with index, cloth, £4.50.

Gleanings in Genesis
A W Pink
Moody

Pink has become a firm favourite with many preachers. His commentaries are full of application. He is thoroughly at home here, and teems with practical lessons from lives and events. With the steep price increase of British books in the last two or three years, these once expensive Moody titles are now extremely good value. This is a must for the Genesis shelf. 408 pages, cloth, £4.40, TB £3.40.

Paradise to Prison
John J Davis
Baker

This is the first in a series of fine commentaries by Dr Davis, who has picked up the historical survey style followed by Edersheim and in recent years, Charles Pfeiffer. However, he handles it very much better to give a highly effective bird's eye view of whatever period he is covering. He makes full use of the latest archaeological discoveries, and his work is rich in background material. Spiritual lessons are weak, but even without them the narrative is so well done that numerous teaching themes will be suggested to the mind of a preacher as he reads. The work is absolutely faithful to Scripture, the prose enjoyable, and the whole liberally supplied with illustrations. Difficult passages are handled very well. 362 pages, cloth, £4.95, TB£4.30.

Commentary on Genesis   Zondervan
J P Lange

Note that the Genesis section in the set of Lange commentaries is generally agreed to be one of the very finest treatments of Genesis available. (See entry under "Whole Bible").

History of Joseph   BT
George Lawson

First issued as "Lectures on Joseph" this is a first rate commentary on Genesis 37 to 49. John Brown said of all Lawson's works, "He has rendered subjects, apparently barren, full of instruction." 320 pages, cloth, £2.50.

Types in Genesis   Kregel
Andrew Jukes

If users can forebear the pompous, pious style of dear old Jukes (and his excesses) they will agree that he teaches the art of seeing Christ in Genesis. Preachers will find here a wealth of suggestive material. While on the one hand, they may wish that Jukes had studied the rules for interpretation of Scripture, on the other, they will find he adds considerably to their messages! Very good value. 421 pages, cloth, £3.50, TB £2.95.

Genesis: A Study Guide Commentary   Zondervan
Leon Wood

Very sane, warm and helpful. Not long — a fine outline. Professor Wood was a great baptist scholar and a real contender for the faith. 152 pages, paper, £1.55, TB £1.25.

The Genesis Flood   Baker
J C Whitcomb/H M Morris

This well known creationist work, (issued 1961; now in 23rd print) focusses on the evidence for, and implications of, the Deluge, demonstrating that this can account for so much that is taken by evolutionists as evidence for their views. Most recent books and booklets vindicating the literal Genesis account of creation owe everything (or practically everything) to this work. So, as the major exposition of the possible scientific significance of the Deluge, it is listed here. 518 pages, paper, £3.90, TB £2.80.

Unformed and Unfilled   Baker
W W Fields

"Did the earth actually become a ruined chaos sometime after its original creation? Were dinosaurs and other creatures killed and fossilized at this time, so that Adam and Eve would find themselves walking, as it were, upon a graveyard of extinct animals?" So asks Dr John Whitcomb in introducing this detailed challenge of the "Gap Theory" of Genesis 1. Many today hold this interpretation — an early disruption, a void ruled by Satan — and then a recreation with Adam and Eve. (Even Berkhof and Pink expound this view.) The author has seemingly covered everything in refuting the Gap Theory (and the Day-Age Theory) from technical and scientific approaches, 245 pages, paper, £3.10, TB £2.35.

Notes

Among out of print classics to watch for, the commentary by James G Murphy (1863) is very full of matter. The comments in John Kitto's "Daily Readings" and Alfred Edersheim's works are well worth having. Also "Christ is All" by Henry Law, though it is very dated and sometimes "overdone" is a glorious and forceful preaching of Christ in the Old Testament. (Banner of Truth used to have the Genesis part in paperback. Exodus is still available).

H C Leupold's commentary on Genesis (Baker) is very helpful, technically, but the homiletical hints are somewhat predictable and it must therefore slide into place behind the classical commentaries. In view of the approximate £10 cost of the 2 volume set, we have delisted the respected Lutheran theologian.

A new commentary currently being promoted is "The Genesis Record" by H M Morris (Baker/EP). Unfortunately the stature Dr Morris has as a scientist does not help in the compilation of a commentary. While faithful and earnest throughout, the comment seldom rises above the obvious. Problem passages are not resolved and while described as 'devotional' there is really very little application or experimental content. The esteemed author is much to be preferred in the scientific field.

A brief summary of the four evangelical approaches to the process and time scale of creation is found on page 134 etc of J Barton Payne's "The Theology of the Older Testament" (Zondervan). Dr Payne comes (we think) to the wrong conclusions, but sets out the views very clearly. (See Old Testament section of Reading List).

We include works that are strong on 'types' not because preachers will want to develop an overstretched presentation of types, but because these commentaries are always rich in overall application of Pentateuch events. The attitude of those ancient people, and the blessings urged upon them, so closely parallel the attitude of modern man to God, and the blessings of the Gospel, that they provide a powerful basis for evangelistic preaching. Candlish, Pink and Jukes are much more helpful here than the more formal Leupold etc.

For the best and clearest discussion of the integrity of the Flood narrative in Genesis (in relation to the Babylonian Flood Epic) see "Archaeology and the Old Testament" by M F Unger. Very useful points are also made by Eugene H Merrill in "An Historical Survey of the Old Testament". (Unger is listed in the Old Testament Section of the Reading List).

Exodus

Gleanings in Exodus   Moody
A W Pink

The comments under "Gleanings in Genesis" apply here. Ten years ago W J Grier qualified his recommendation of Pink in these words, ". . . always of devotional value but some of his interpretations need checking against those of better-trained exegetes." However, Pink is always outstanding for suggesting application for preachers. Unlike all the other "Gleanings" volumes this one is set in very small type, double column, but it means we have the value of a much larger commentary in the same format. 384 pages, cloth, £4.40, TB £3.40.

Devotional Commentary on Exodus   Kregel
F B Meyer

Meyer was a pulpiteer, not a commentator. But as one who was at his best with Bible-biographies, there is an abundance of material here, with a great deal of application. This must be rated as the best life of Moses in print. Two volumes in one: cloth, £6.15, TB £4.75.

Moses and the Gods of Egypt   Baker
John J Davis

Studies in the Book of Exodus. (See comment under Genesis — Paradise to Prison). Much interesting background (the "Rods and Serpents" treatment of Exodus 17 is unique). Very good section on early-or-late Exodus date; Dr Davis stands with the biblical early date. Complete with illustrations, tabernacle drawings etc. 331 pages, paper, £3.00, TB £2.40.

The Tabernacle of God in the Wilderness of Sinai   Zondervan
Paule Kiene

This book is just stunning for its beauty and attention to detail. The author has reconstructed in scale the Tabernacle and all its furnishings. Over 40 colour photographs (with descriptive text) cover the proceedings of sacrifice and worship. Looking at these superb, lifelike photographs is the nearest we shall come to a real apprehension of what it was like to be there. First published 1978, cloth, £9.26, TB £7.25.

The Holy Vessels and Furniture of the Tabernacle   Kregel
Henry Soltau

This famous old work has ten colour plates far inferior to the above listed work, but there is more text with devotional comments and some lessons drawn. 148 pages, cloth, £3.60, TB £2.95.

The Tabernacle, the Priesthood and the Offerings   Kregel
Henry Soltau

A bigger work packed with information and suggested practical application. Worth any commentary on Exodus and Leviticus. Extremely readable and very good value. 474 pages, cloth, £3.60, TB £2.95.

The Gospel in Exodus   BT
Henry Law

Part of "Christ Is All". Old fashioned preaching which sees pictures of Christ everywhere. Not to be imitated, but to be deeply respected and learned from. It will provoke preachers to modify and update its material for evangelistic preaching. 176 pages, paper, 50p.

Notes

The "Exodus Problem" by D A Courville (on the date of the Exodus) is far too big a work for most preachers on this issue. The right balance is struck in the relevant chapters of "Archaeology and the Old Testament" (Unger), "Survey of Israel's History" (Wood) and the John Davis commentaries. (See the Old Testament section in the Reading List). Unger has the best way of contrasting the early-late viewpoint arguments.

A classic discussion of the hardening of Pharaoh's heart with an explanation of each reference is found in Alfred Edersheim's "The Exodus and the Wanderings in the Wilderness" (pages 58-63).

Among out-of-print works it is possible that Thomas Millington's "Signs and Wonders in the Land of Ham" (a description of the ten plagues of Egypt) will be reprinted in 1979 in the USA. James Murphy's "Commentary on Exodus" (1866) is still seen second-hand and is a treasure. James Hamilton's "Moses the Man of God" is a great work which will suggest approaches to preachers. But with Davis, Soltau, Pink and Meyer we are highly favoured for helps.

Leviticus

The Law of the Offerings   **Kregel**
Andrew Jukes

Some dislike the verbosity and brethreny style. But Spurgeon called this a "very condensed, instructive, refreshing book. It will open up new trains of thought . . . in the teaching of the types." No one else explains the significance of the Levitical offerings (in relation to Calvary) as Jukes does here. Bear with the book's painfully repetitive start. Suddenly it bursts out with rich things. 219 pages, paper, £2.15, TB £1.65.

Leviticus   **BT/also Baker**
Andrew A Bonar

This superb commentary by the great Scots divine is a clear and unfanciful guide through the complexities of Leviticus. It is full of warm spiritual application. An essential tool for preachers. Banner of Truth have a cloth edition at £4.50 and Baker a paperback (528 pages) at £4.40, TB £3.35.

Notes

The old "Expositor's Bible" volume on Leviticus by Samuel Kellog has been reprinted by Klock and Klock and is available in the UK at over £9, but Bonar is more satisfying and nearly £5 cheaper for a bigger book.

Numbers

Numbers, Journey to God's Rest-land   **Moody**
Irving Jensen

In the "Everyman's" series this brief popular commentary is

straightforward and useful. Dr Jensen must be read by preachers embarking on a treatment of the Journeyings. Though brief, there is considerable application suggested. 128 pages, paper, £1.40, TB £1.05.

Numbers   Baker
K E Jones
This small commentary is a very good guide though another book neglected by commentators. A little flimsy in one or two places (such as Balaam's ass) but a good workmanlike guide with good explanations of most problem chapters. (Full of suggested application). 90 pages, paper, £1.20, TB £0.90.

Notes

In view of the shortage of commentaries on Numbers the following are listed as old copies may still be found, and they are being considered for reprinting:—

Church in the Wilderness   *(Out of Print)*
W. Seaton

2 volumes (1821 etc). A very fine treatment of the wanderings of the children of Israel with much application. This is a classic, and has been taken up at our request for reprinting in the USA. We hope it will appear during 1979.

The Wanderings Of The Children Of Israel   *(Out of Print)*
George Wagner

(1862 etc) Another work alongside Seaton recommended by Spurgeon. These two works will bring the journeyings to life for preachers. This may also be reprinted and should be watched for.

Deuteronomy

Deuteronomy   Moody
Samuel Schultz

A most useful brief commentary from a modern writer in the "Everyman's" series. The complex laws are well explained and shown to have great positive value. This work includes considerable information not readily found elsewhere. Dr Schultz is Professor of Bible at Wheaton College. 127 pages, paper, £1.40, TB £1.05.

Joshua, Judges

Gleanings in Joshua
A W Pink
Moody

See notes on Pink under Genesis and Exodus. This was his last work. Reprinted twelve times. Worth a great deal to preachers. 429 pages, cloth, £4.40, TB £3.40.

Conquest and Crisis
John J Davis
Baker

Studies in Joshua, Judges and Ruth by the Vice-President of Grace College and Theological Seminary, Winona Lake. Excellent survey of events. See note on author's work under Genesis and Exodus. 170 pages, paper, £1.85, TB £1.40.

The Book of Joshua
Wm G Blaikie
Klock

Originally the Joshua part of the Expositor's Bible. Very good if a little dated in style. (His volume on David, now out of print, is a classic.) With Pink this is all a preacher could possibly want. 416 pages, cloth, £7.25, TB £5.25.

Distressing Days of the Judges
Leon Wood
Zondervan

We strongly recommend the late Prof Leon Wood's work. In an area where credible commentaries are so few this is absolutely sound; conservative in dating and harmony; and full of spiritual application. It has no British counterpart. 434 pages, cloth, £6.15, TB £4.75.

Lange's Commentary
Zondervan

The Commentary on Joshua is by Pastor F R Fay; and that on Judges and Ruth by Prof Paulus Cassel. These are very detailed in exegesis, and (the last two in particular) very helpful in the "homiletical and practical" sections. (See Whole Bible).

Notes

Calvin on Joshua is sometimes seen second-hand. The Eerdmans reprints, no longer produced, are still to be found. Look out for "The Judges" in "Daily Bible Illustrations" by Kitto (last printed 1905). Also, try to secure "Men of Faith: or Sketches from the Book of Judges" by Luke Wiseman, Hodder 1874, "Powerful style. He was one of the best preachers in the Wesleyan body" —

CHS. This work is full of inspiring applied portraits.

An unusual work is, "The Valour of Faith, or, the Gospel in the Life of Gideon" by G A Rogers, (pub 1859). It is full of application. "Lectures on the Book of Ruth" by George Lawson (1805, etc), is the only really good volume on this book. There is

A R Fausset on Judges is rather heavy and the Klock reprint is now out of print at the publishers.

Arthur Cundall on Judges (Tyndale/IVP) puts himself into absurd difficulties which he cannot solve by selling himself to liberal chronological views. His bibliography tells all.

Samuel, Kings, Chronicles

I and II Samuel   Klock
William G Blaikie

In reprinting these volumes the Messrs Klock have made available one of the best portions of the very variable "Expositor's Bible" series. Issued 1887-8. Prof Blaikie was one of those ministers who (with the Bonars) left the established church in Scotland at the Disruption. These two volumes are among the best work available on I & II Samuel as far as preachers are concerned. I Sam: 440 pages, cloth, £7.30, TB £5.35. II Sam: 400 pages, cloth, £6.85, TB £4.85. The set £14.00, TB £10.20.

The Birth of a Kingdom   Baker
John J Davis

Studies in I-II Samuel and I Kings. Another in the same series as "Conquest and Crisis" (above). Extremely useful as a "background" commentary. 209 page treatment of David; his fugitive period; Saul; the witch of Endor passage; the enigma of Solomon — all these are handled very well indeed. Dr Davis is a master of brevity. (Many illustrations). 190 pages , paper, £2.50, TB £1.85.

Solomon to the Exile—Studies in Kings & Chronicles   Baker
J C Whitcomb Jnr

Many preachers already have the well-known chronological charts from Dr Whitcomb and know of his co-authorship of the Genesis Flood. This book (in the same series as those of J J Davis) is a little lighter in style but continues the system of blending a summary of events with much background and archaeological material. Infinitely more readable than most histories of this Old Testament period. Very useful. 182 pages, paper, £2.00, TB £1.40.

A Harmony of Samuel, Kings and Chronicles   Baker
William D. Crockett

Another basic tool for the preacher's library. Not a commentary but a fine harmony, the value of which will be obvious. The various passages are run out in parallel columns — not merged into a continuous flow of text. Contains good notes, and will successfully unravel these books for preachers and teachers. 365 pages, cloth, £4.95, TB £3.75.

Lights and Shadows in the Life of King David   PPH
Charles Vince

Adapted from addresses dealing with certain times of triumph and blessing and times of tragedy and failure. Although not covering all the life of David by any means, this volume is a great help to the preacher. It is a great example of experimental teaching of the Word. (This work was highly commended by CHS who told the Pastors' College students that this was the highest order of preaching). Due January 1979, paper, £2.10, £1.70.

Elijah the Tishbite   Baker
F W Krummacher

Reprinted numerous times over the last 100 years. (An RTS best seller in 1870). A great study; highly readable. Used as a commentary it is of tremendous value to preachers. It is full of applicatory themes. Adapted from sermons given in Germany. In fact, infinitely more valuable to preachers than a formal commentary. 458 pages, paper, £2.35, TB £1.85.

Elisha: A Prophet for our Times   Baker
F W Krummacher

Both this and the above must be on the preacher's shelves. Here is warm, experimental communication which will inspire God's spokesmen and set a great example. We think that anything by Dr Krummacher is worth its weight in gold to preachers. 251 pages, paper, £1.60, TB £1.10.

First and Second Kings   Moody
Richard McNeely

Another shorter commentary, this is a useful guide through the books with many explanations, though not much applicatory or experimental material. However, where commentaries are light a combination of Krummacher's volumes on Elijah and Elisha, and a little modern work like this to untangle the incidental detail, would amount to a great asset in the library. 158 pages, paper, £1.60, TB £1.20.

Commentaries — Samuel, Kings, Chronicles

Lange on I & II Kings   **Zondervan**

The Commentary on I & II Kings in this series is by Dr Bahr. Says Spurgeon, "It must have cost a great effort to make the homiletical part of this volume as good as it is. It is a treasury to the preacher, and is all the more precious because we have next to nothing upon the books of the Kings." (See under Whole Bible).

Notes

The following excellent Bible-biographies are worth their weight in gold to preachers. They are all still seen second-hand (especially Wm Taylor) and Lawson and MacDuff on Naaman are candidates for reprinting with one publisher:—

John Kitto's "Daily Readings" series on "Samuel, Saul and David" and "Solomon and the Kings." J A Miller — "Saul the First King of Israel" (Snow 1866). "David, King of Israel, The Divine Plan and Lessons of His Life" Wm G Blaikie (Nisbet 1861 etc). "Discourses on the History of David" George Lawson (Berwick 1833). "David: His Life and its Lessons", Wm M Taylor, (Sampson Low 1875). "The Prophet of Fire" (Elijah), J R MacDuff, (Nisbet 1863). "The Healing Waters, or The Story of Naaman", J R MacDuff, (Nisbet 1873).

Ezra, Nehemiah, Esther

Ezra and Nehemiah   **Moody**
G Coleman Luck

Another in the "Everyman's" series from Moody. This is a popular study, assembling some useful information, but very weak in application. 127 pages, paper, £1.40, TB £1.05.

Notes

At the present time we are largely dependent for these books on the Whole Bible commentaries. Matthew Henry has a mass of warm application on these three books. Matthew Poole is very good, and the excellent coverage in Jamieson, Fausset and Brown is by Dr Robert Jamieson. See also pages 377-411 in Leon Wood — "Survey of Israel's History". The treatment in Lange gives the most useful homiletic advice, but it is surprising how poor the commentaries are on Ezra and Nehemiah when one considers the obvious abundance of practical application to spiritual church building.

George Lawson's "Discourses on Esther" (1804) is superb and should be reprinted. Equally valuable is Thomas McGie's "Lectures on Esther".

Job

Notes on Job   Baker
Albert Barnes

"Exceedingly good. One of the best of this author's generally valuable productions. The student should purchase this work at once as it is absolutely necessary to his library." — Spurgeon. Dr Barnes has rounded up all the views expressed by his time and supplies an abundance of information. He gives the preacher countless leads. Later writers give nothing like as much. 2 volumes, cloth, the set £9.60, TB £6.90.

Lange's Commentary on Job   Zondervan
Otto Zockler

The Job section of the Lange series "contains a large collection of available material, and, if within a minister's means, should be a foundation book in his library. We are very far from endorsing all Zockler's remarks, but the volume is an important one." — Spurgeon. (See Whole Bible).

Sermons from Job   Baker
John Calvin

The twenty sermons reprinted here are a magnificent example of the Reformer's preaching, as well as being a great commentary on the major themes of the book. Here is close subjective application. Due January 1979, 338 pages, paper, £2.95, TB £2.35.

Arguments of the Book of Job Unfolded   Klock
William H Green

William Green was one of the greatest Hebrew scholars and, during a lifetime spent teaching at Princeton from 1864, wrote a famous attack on the higher criticism of the Pentateuch as well as his great work "The Unity of the Book of Genesis" (1895) refuting the documentary theory. This is the nearest Prof Green ever came to a 'popular' study. 375 pages, cloth, £5.75, TB £4.05. ("The Higher Criticism of the Pentateuch" is back in print Jan 1979 from Baker; paper; £2.35).

Job   Moody
Roy Zuck

This new "Everyman's" commentary is written for the layman but its 192 pages contain much useful comment and it is well worth placing alongside the older worthies for supplementary material.

Dr Zuck is often far too light, and misses the point frequently, but still has made a contribution. 192 pages, paper, £1.60, TB £1.20.

Notes

"The Gospel revealed to Job" — 30 lectures by C A Hulbert — another volume which is truly original and suggestive. Long out of print, the Longmans 1853 edition is occasionally seen. See also E J Young's "Introduction to the Old Testament" pages 281-6 and 309-21.

E C Gibson's 1899 work on Job has been reprinted (K & K) but enough seems to be enough. It adds nothing to available material except cost.

Psalms

The Treasury of David   **Zondervan and MacDonald editions**
C H Spurgeon

This famous work contains Spurgeon's own exposition of each Psalm together with his selection of extracts from other writers and masses of preaching suggestions for each one. The Zondervan edition is three large volumes (9½ x 6¼"), cloth bound. It is little more expensive than the small-page, limp bound set also available in the UK, but of far greater quality and worth. No available work (other than Barnes who is not listed here) gives so much detail. Each volume over 480 pages, The set £28, TB £18.50.

The Psalms Translated and Explained   **Baker**
J A Alexander

All J A Alexander's commentaries are full, scholarly, yet heavily endowed with application. This is no exception. It will give great satisfaction to the preacher. Cloth, £4.95, TB £4.50.

Psalms   **BT**
William S Plumer

An enormous book in which this nineteenth century American preacher and schoolman collects the best comments from other writers. In the same style as the author's volume on Romans, there are very long sections of numbered doctrinal and practical remarks which are of prime importance to preachers and teachers. Cloth, £8.50.

Christ and His Church in the Book of Psalms   **Kregel**
Andrew Bonar

"Of the highest order of merit. The author does not strain the text, but gives its real meaning. His remarks are always weighty, spiritual and suggestive" — Spurgeon. The closest friend and biographer of Murray M'Cheyne, Andrew Bonar was a great scholar, preacher and stalwart defender of the faith. Not a verse-by-verse commentary; rather 2-4 pages of discussion on each psalm, emphasising the references to Christ and His redeemed people. An important 'second' commentary. 457 pages, cloth, £7.00, TB £5.95.

Psalms   EP
H C Leupold

First published 1959 this exposition from a conservative Lutheran scholar is absolutely faithful. Leupold is always warm, though he is straightjacketed by his modern style of commenting. He does not roam into much application and his homiletic 'hints' are rather weak. However this is an important exposition and very good value. 970 pages, cloth, £6.95.

Psalms   Moody
Robt L Alden

"Everyman's" series, 3 volumes divide the Psalms into songs of devotion, dedication and discipleship. Trite in places but good on the whole, and especially useful for bringing up-to-date background information alongside the older commentaries. Paper, the set, £4.20, TB £3.15.

Exposition of the Psalms   Eerdmans
Augustine

Spurgeon says, "Too frequently mystical and confounds plain texts. No theological library is complete without this work, for there are grand thoughts in it like huge nuggets." (Nicene & Post-Nicene Fathers, Series 1, Vol 8). Perhaps only for men who already possess everything else! 683 pages, cloth, £5.80, TB £4.50.

Notes

Prof James Murphy's work on the Psalms has been reprinted in the USA and is available for around £8. This is a fine commentary but even with 702 pages it does not add enough to the above to fully justify its price. Cloth, £9.95, TB £7.95.

David Dickson's great commentary in three volumes was originally called "A brief explanation of the Psalms"! Banner of Truth reprinted it, in one volume, but it is not now available. An old Banner copy is worth looking for as it is highly stimulating to preachers. It has been replaced on the Banner list by William Plumer's volume on Psalms.

Proverbs, Ecclesiastes, Songs

Proverbs   **BT**
Charles Bridges

According to Spurgeon, "The best work on Proverbs . . . very suggestive to ministers." W J Grier seems more cautious, saying, ". . . attractive and useful to the general reader but for exegesis he needs supplementing." Bridges does seem to miss a deeper evaluation of many proverbs because they just remind him of a basic doctrine or truth, which he promptly expounds instead. But it is vital in another area so short of expositions. 640 pages, cloth, £3.50.

Studies in Proverbs   **Kregel**
Wm Arnot

This is "Laws from Heaven for Life on Earth." Says Spurgeon, "The passages which he dilates upon are set in a clear and beautiful light. For a happy blending of illustrative faculty, practical sound sense, and spirituality, Dr Arnot was almost unrivalled." A series of homely homilies of varying quality. Most will stir the faculties of preachers, but only certain proverbs or groups of proverbs are picked out for attention. A good second to Bridges. 583 pages, cloth, £5.95, TB £5.10.

Ecclesiastes   **Baker**
H C Leupold

A very good modern commentary from the American Lutheran scholar. As usual not enough suggested application, but still an essential commentary. Cloth, £3.80, TB £2.80.

Song of Solomon   **BT**
George Burrowes

A standard commentary first published in the USA in 1853. Complete with much application this is everything we need. 532 pages, cloth, £3.00.

Notes

Volume 7 of "The Biblical Museum" by James Comper Gray contains Proverbs, Ecclesiastes and Song of Solomon. It is quite superb in these books, giving numerous illustrations, anecdotes, and helpful quotations. Much of the material is hopelessly dated, and some is so pious and Victorian as to be amusing, but there is so much here that the work is still a treasure-store for teachers and preachers.

One need hardly say that Matthew Henry is found absolutely in his element with these books.

Isaiah

Isaiah   Eerdmans
Edward J Young

In three volumes, this is the ultimate commentary on Isaiah. "Concluding the manuscript of his third volume on Isaiah shortly before his death in February 1968, Prof Young was able to lay the copestone on this his most outstanding commentary. He will be long remembered as a careful and most helpful exegete." — W J Grier.

This is a great work from one of the finest conservative scholars of our time. Total of 1717 pages, cloth, the set £19.50, TB £15.50.

The Prophecies of Isaiah   Zondervan
J A Alexander

This work received the strongest commendation from Spurgeon. Very clear, 2 volumes in one, 874 pages, cloth, £9.25, TB £7.25.

Barnes' Notes on Isaiah, 2 volumes   Baker

Barnes is not altogether outdated. Though surpassed by Alexander and almost rendered obsolete by Young, yet there remains a pithy, practical usefulness in the approach of Barnes and he has many points and explanations which the others do not give. Cloth, the set £11.70, TB £8.95.

The Gospel of Isaiah   Moody
Allan MacRae

This is a study of chapters 40-56. The material is unusual and follows the theme of the title. Introduction by Francis Schaeffer. 192 pages, paper £1.90, TB £1.45.

Notes

H C Leupold's exposition of Isaiah is good, but with E J Young available, it is much more advisable to save for the larger work.

Jeremiah

Jeremiah   Concordia
Theodore Laetsch

Passing from Isaiah to Jeremiah there is an inexplicable

disappearance of commentaries. This commentary, from a Lutheran scholar, provides a vital storehouse of exegetical information. While not very suggestive, it is so full as to provide the preacher with all he requires. But he must use his own flair to discern the themes and applications. Paper, £5.25.

Jeremiah and Lamentations   **Moody**
Irving L Jensen

This short, American commentary designed for the layman is of great value because of the shortage of Jeremiah material. Dr Jensen takes a premillennial view of the Restoration passages and is shallow in places, but he analyses the book very efficiently, relates the fulfilled prophecies to their historic events, and suggests applications. A warm study from a stalwart Bible School teacher. 180 pages, paper, £1.40, TB £1.05.

Lange's Commentary   **Zondervan**

The Jeremiah-Lamentations volume in the set is by Dr C W Nagelsbach. Spurgeon quotes approvingly a review which said, "Whoever becomes possessed of this great work will have, in a comprehensive form, the results of all ancient and modern exegesis." (See Whole Bible).

Notes

The Messianic passages in Jeremiah are expounded by Hengstenberg in his Christology of the Old Testament (pages 617-673 in Kregel edition). Where commentaries are few, the "Whole-Bible" commentaries seem to rise to the task. Matthew Henry is very sensitive on Jeremiah; Jamieson, Fausset and Brown is at its best. Once again, readers will be greatly profited by reference to E J Young's "Introduction to the Old Testament" (p 223) and Leon Wood's Survey of Israel's History (p 200). Unfortunately no commentary takes up the great evangelistic arguments which are surely the principal feature of the first half of this book — a handbook of heartfelt appeals.

Ezekiel

Ezekiel
From the scarcity of Jeremiah commentaries we move to the total lack of acceptable Ezekiel studies. Calvin (who only reached chapter 20 before his death) is out of print. So are the best nineteenth century exegetes. Aside from Lange and Keil (who are very informative but rather dry here) and other Whole-Bible

commentaries, there is nothing available worth having. H L Ellison is too appalling to be taken seriously as an evangelical exegete. The Tyndale IVP commentary suffers from all the weaknesses of the series. While we can sometimes find help from one or two popular-style American paperback studies, in Ezekiel they completely succumb to dispensational matter. The only real hope is to locate one of the out-of-print works, or hope that the reprint publishers will be persuaded to fill this important gap.

Exposition of Ezekiel
Patrick Fairbairn

(T & T Clark, 1851 and many reprints). Copies of the last issue of this work by American Sovereign Grace Publishers are sometimes seen second-hand, though T & T Clark copies are very rare. Spurgeon said, "Dr Fairbairn has a cool judgement and a warm heart."

Daniel

Prophecy of Daniel   BT
Edward J Young

Alongside Calvin on Daniel this is the best. The treatment of the prophetic passages is so clear and spiritually rich it will be greatly appreciated by preachers, 334 pages, cloth, £3.50.

Barnes' Notes on Daniel   Baker
J A Barnes

Old fashioned — and largely rendered obsolete by a superb commentary like that of Prof Young. But many men are used to Barnes and find themselves stimulated by his method. These volumes have an amazing amount of information in them. Cloth, the set: £8.00, TB £6.75.

Studies in the Book of Daniel   Baker
Robert Dick Wilson

A reprint of the work of this great scholar is coming about June 1979. Robert Dick Wilson was one of the few who left Princeton at its downgrade crisis to found Westminster Theological Seminary. No price details yet to hand.

Darius the Mede   Baker
John C Whitcomb

A well reasoned paper arguing that Gubaru, Governor of Babylon, was Darius the Mede. Subtitled, "The Historical Chronology of Daniel", its 84 pages introduce the reader to the data and literature surrounding Daniel and the period of Darius. 84 pages, paper, 95p TB 75p.

Notes

Calvin on Daniel is exceptional, though only second-hand volumes are now available. H C Leupold is good, though not listed here as E J Young should satisfy. The old work by E B Pusey is being reprinted in America and is (astonishingly) described by the publisher as "one of the strongest conservative commentaries". It is certainly not that, and in the context of what is now available, would be a waste of any preacher's money and time.

One very fine work which may possibly be reprinted in the USA during 1979 is entitled "Daniel: Statesman and Prophet." This was issued last century by the RTS. Its author was never named, though he was a leading evangelical preacher of the time. The book's biographical treatment of Daniel is exceptional and it includes a long section on "The Angel of the Covenant", which is the best straightforward treatment of the theophanies to be found anywhere. This wonderful volume is quite common second-hand — as so many reprints were made — but a modern reprint will be of great value.

Minor Prophets

The Minor Prophets   Baker
Homer Hailey

A modern commentary from a former professor at Florida College. This is a fine explanation of the books from a member of the 'spiritual Israel-application' school. The great prophecies, say of Zech 12, are shown to refer not to a physical Jerusalem, but the spiritual Jerusalem of the New Testament church in the Gospel age. A most carefully executed and spiritual commentary. 428 pages, cloth £4.30, TB £3.30.

Four Minor Prophets   Moody
Frank Gaebelein

A devotional commentary on Obadiah, Jonah, Habakkuk and Haggai. While strongly premillennial, Dr Gaebelein is not so much concerned about these themes here. This is a warm, uncomplicated study. While not "deep", the preacher will be pleased with the emphasis on suggested applications. 253 pages, paper, £2.50, TB £1.95.

The heavier exposition from the evangelical Lutheran camp. For those lacking Lange or Keil, this more modern work will be as much as is required. Paper, £6.25.

Notes

Commenting on the Minor Prophets section of the Keil and Delitzsch commentaries Spurgeon approvingly quotes the words of a reviewer — "Dr Keil is at his best in this commentary; and to all who have ventured in this obscure region we can promise an intelligent guide and a serviceable light in this work."

If old copies of Jeremiah Burroughes on Hosea can be referred to, the preacher will find wonderful examples of applied comment. Also, in the works of Richard Sibbes, his famous sermon "The Returning Backslider" on Hosea 14, will yield a moving example.

Amos   BT
Ray Beeley

An applied commentary of far greater value than its price and format would suggest. 117 pages, paper, 60p.

The Prophet Jonah   BT
Hugh Martin

First published 1870. Dr Hugh Martin was one of the great preachers of the mid nineteenth century in Scotland. This treatment of the life of Jonah is gripping to read. Totally unlike a commentary in its 'flow' it is packed with spiritual application. There is nothing better. 359 pages, cloth, £3.00

Note

Many past worthies have dealt with the life of Jonah. First was Calvin, whose "Lectures upon the Prophet Jonas" are a masterpiece of portrait study. If only this could be reprinted. Then the prolific "illustrator" Joseph Exell issued a volume of "Practical Readings . . ." which are still often seen in old book shops. Patrick Fairbairn produced a well known volume which was reprinted recently by Kregel, but has gone out of print again. Time would fail to tell of Thomas Fuller, Dr Peddie — and so many others. Jonah is a real favourite with the worthies of the past — but Banner have chosen the best (next to Calvin) for reprinting. No preacher can fail with such a subject, and such a heritage of help. The modern popular work "Jonah the Reluctant Prophet" by Wm Banks (Moody) only proves that you cannot add much to Hugh Martin without being trivial.

Zechariah   BT

T V Moore

Sane and detailed, this is surely the best commentary the Banner of Truth could have selected for reprinting, providing a reasonable minimum of textual discussion, but with the most clear and spiritual explanations of the figures. 251 pages, cloth, £2.50.

Zechariah   EP

H C Leupold

Another very good, detailed commentary from Dr Leupold for preachers who require a technically more intensive study than T V Moore, and who lack Lange or Keil. Not as suggestive as T V Moore, cloth, £2.75.

Haggai and Malachi   BT

T V Moore

Of the same rich quality as the author's Zechariah. 180 pages, cloth, £2.00.

Notes

(Zechariah occupies a very large portion of Hengstenberg's Christology. See pages 262-401 of the Kregel edition.)

Ebenezer Henderson's work "The Twelve Minor Prophets" (issue 1845) is being reprinted in 1979 by Baker, but be warned — it is dull, dry and attempts no prophetic spiritual application.

New Testament: General

Barnes' Notes on the New Testament Kregel
Albert Barnes

As the publishers state, every word of Barnes is included. This is a beautiful production and frankly makes nonsense of the multi-volume edition also available which costs over £49 a set. Barnes (1798-1870) was a prominent American Presbyterian. While a strong Calvinist, he nevertheless held to unlimited atonement, and suffered a heresy trial on account of this. His "Notes" are full of information, and he summarises the views of all the key expositors up to his time. Regular users grow very attached to these notes, which are especially valuable to preachers. 1 volume, large format, 1761 pages, cloth, £14.20, TB £11.50.

New Testament Word Studies Kregel
J A Bengel

This is, of course, Bengel's famous "Gnomon of the New Testament" but Kregel have changed the title. Says Spurgeon, "Men with a dislike for thinking had better not purchase the precious volumes, for they will be of little use to them; but men who love brain work will find fine exercise in spelling out the deep meaning of Bengel's excessively terse sentences." In these studies, Bengel "condenses more matter into a line than can be extracted from pages of other writers." This has been in print since 1742. Complete in 2 large volumes, cloth, £18.60, TB £14.50.

Lange Commentaries Zondervan
Prof J J Von Oosterzee

The Lange series are extremely good on the Gospels. Each 'block' of verses treated is dealt with under the headings — Exegetical and Critical, Doctrinal and Ethical, Homiletical and Practical. (See Whole Bible).

A Harmony of the Gospels St AP
John Calvin

Calvin's commentary on Matthew, Mark and Luke takes these three Gospels and treats them as harmony. This is Calvin at his best. The Torrance edition is a modern translation. Calvin stands above all subsequent commentators for brevity, clarity and sheer readability. If anyone has a prejudice against the great expositor, use of these commentaries will soon dispel it. Three volumes (Vol

III includes the Epistles of James and Jude). Volume 1, 316 pages; Volume 2, 297 pages; Volume 3, 336 pages, cloth, £3.50 each.

The Suffering Saviour   Moody
F W Krummacher

As the cross is the focal point of the New Testament this outstanding work must be listed here. A great classic with all the melting force of Krummacher. (Bickersteth was born-again as a lad through this work.) German generosity of words, but incomparable as a model of feelingful instruction. The importance of this work to preachers cannot be underestimated. It should be read before almost anything else. This is preaching! The Moody Wycliffe edition is a large-type, really high quality book. (It is not the same as the Baker edition which costs the same. That is a very much smaller format, uneven reprint of a nineteenth century work.) 444 pages, paper, £5.10, TB £2.50.

Seven Sayings of the Saviour on the Cross   Baker
A W Pink

Highlights the deep significance of every step and word of Christ at the time of the atonement. Calvary-preaching will be the centre and soul of all our work, therefore studies like this are essential. 134 pages, paper, 90p, TB 70p.

Miracles of our Saviour   Kregel
William M Taylor

Dr Taylor was Minister of the Broadway Tabernacle, New York (a contemporary of Spurgeon) in a great preaching age. These messages bear his style very heavily, and so are not complete expositions but are of great value to preachers. Particularly helpful in stimulating evangelistic thoughts. 449 pages, cloth, £3.70, TB £2.95.

Parables of our Saviour   Kregel
William M Taylor

See comment above. Taylor was born in Scotland (1829) and preached in Britain for many years before emigrating to the USA. Like "Miracles" this work is a real help in the preparation of evangelistic ministry. 449 pages, cloth, £3.70, TB £2.95.

Exposition of the Parables   Kregel
Benjamin Keach

Spurgeon playfully accuses Keach of making "metaphors run on as many legs as a centipede." So he does — but the book is stored up to the full with hints and inspiration for preachers. This is how the parables were preached by English Baptists in the 17th Century. Value for money in this huge reprint from Kregel. 891 pages, cloth, £8.00, TB £6.50.

The Life and Times of Jesus the Messiah   Eerdmans
Alfred Edersheim

Without doubt the best work of its kind. Edersheim was the greatest authority on Jewish customs and affairs so that background information in the work is of great importance. (His tracing of the Passion sequence of events is unique). A standard reference work. (This must not be confused with a MacDonald edition in very poor type and format distributed in the UK by Evangelical Press). 828 pages, cloth, £8.50, TB £6.50.

New Light on the Gospels   Baker
Clifford Wilson

Dr Wilson gives fascinating information about very early documents and portions of Scripture manuscripts found in recent years, which throw confirmatory light on passages in the Gospels. A source of valuable information and illustration. 128 pages, paper, 90p, TB 60p.

A Harmony of the Gospels   P&R
Loraine Boettner

A practical aid for tracing the order of events and bringing together all the recorded details of any event. The four Gospels are presented as one narrative in the American Standard Version Text. The headings for the events and discourses are very clear and a text index enables the user to trace the location of any Gospel verse. This is the most inexpensive and useful harmony available. 132 pages, paper, £1.85, TB £1.35.

Parables of our Lord   Baker
C H Spurgeon

Here, in one book, are all the published sermons on the parables. Once again the work provides a commentary and a demonstration of evangelistic application. This arrangement of sermons cannot be too highly commended to preachers. Baker aim to produce the volume early in 1979. Paper (about) TB £4.30.

Miracles of our Lord   Baker
C H Spurgeon

Baker are to be commended for the reprinting of these two volumes. They are Spurgeon's published sermons on miracles grouped together under each miracle. This presentation constitutes a powerful preachers' commentary (especially where Spurgeon preached on the same miracle several times over a period of thirty five years). The preaching of evangelistic messages is completely demonstrated here. These two volumes are expected to appear early in 1979. Paper (about) TB £2.85 each.

New Light on New Testament Letters Baker
Clifford Wilson

A similar little book to "New Light on the Gospels" (see comment). Well worth a preacher's time, it contains information drawn from documents and practices of Bible-times society which throw light on passages in the Epistles, "deacon" for example, technically means no more than "servant". But before New Testament times temple and ceremonial officials were often called "deacons", indicating that the word signified much more than its bare dictionary meaning. This is but one among a random collection of different items of information from this noted scholar. 125 pages, paper, 85p, TB 60p.

The Schilder Trilogy Baker
Klaas Schilder

See listing under Reading List, New Testament. This very big work on the Passion has been offered (3 vol) casebound at £24.85. If men require it, we feel the high quality 3 vol paperback from Baker is better value at £15.50, TB £11.95.

Notes

R C Trench on Miracles and Parables are not listed here. Though once recommended by Spurgeon (who warned of the errors present) these volumes have diminished in usefulness with the arrival of much better material. Bishop Trench was an Anglo-Catholic with little evangelical light or sympathy and his work will hardly stimulate the preacher with regard to application and Gospel fervour.

Matthew

Matthew BT
William Hendriksen

The Hendriksen Commentaries are now very well known and greatly appreciated. Dr Hendriksen's style is clear and all his comment is applied. He is a father in the Reformed faith. It is only necessary to supplement Hendriksen for help in preaching an evangelistic application. 1015 pages with bibliography, cloth, £5.50.

Matthew — Genius of the Gospel   Kregel
David Thomas

Subtitled, "Homiletical Commentary", Spurgeon said of this, "We hardly know a more suggestive book." This will be published March 1979 and will be a great preaching aid. Cloth, £8.00, TB £5.95.

Matthew   St AP
John Calvin

See "A Harmony Of The Gospels" above.

Spurgeon's Popular Exposition of Matthew   Baker
C H Spurgeon

This was the last work from Spurgeon's pen and was published after his death. It is an unusual commentary taking up the Matthew emphasis on the Saviour as King. It is not really a preacher's commentary, and yet it breathes such a spirit that much can be derived from it. A reprint will appear early 1979 from Baker 272 pages, paper, £2.60, TB £1.85.

Exposition of the Sermon on the Mount   Baker
A W Pink

This series of studies is richly applied in the author's typical manner and merits a place on the preacher's Matthew shelf. Cloth, £4.80, TB £3.20. (Or EP paperback edition at £2.95.)

The Beatitudes   BT
Thomas Watson

This is a wonderful example of applied Puritan teaching. Heart-searching and full of illustrations this really should be consulted before one embarks on preaching Matthew 5. Most preachers will find themselves prescribing it frequently to others. 307 pages, cloth, £2.50.

Notes

Regarding "Expository Thoughts on the Gospels" by J C Ryle, the Matthew and Mark volumes of this fine work are not recommended on account of their brevity. Ryle extended his approach by the time he reached Luke, and includes in the later volumes practically everything he says in the earlier ones. Accordingly Luke and John are listed below.

It is worth trying to obtain second-hand R C H Lenski's "Interpretation of Matthew's Gospel". It is a big work which has just gone out of print. A renowned Lutheran expositor, Dr Lenski always contributes much.

Mark

Mark BT
William Hendriksen

Once again, Dr Hendriksen provides a superb commentary with much application. 700 pages with bibliography, cloth, £4.50.

Mark in the Greek New Testament Eerdmans
Kenneth Wuest

Since 1950 these word studies have been appreciated by preachers and teachers. Instead of producing a commentary padded out with flimsy word studies, Dr Wuest concentrated on word studies only. His aim was to explain the full meaning of each word and to show how the word is used in other Greek literature. Key words in each verse are amplified and discussed at good length. Even men in possession of NT Greek will find much help here. Very often a man's understanding of a passage will be entirely altered by appreciating the full meaning of a word. There is also an expanded translation of every verse. All the Wuest word studies are highly recommended and all are now inexpensive in paperback format. 400 pages, paper, £2.10, TB £1.50.

Mark: A Portrait of the Servant Moody
D E Hiebert

Dr Hiebert has been professor of Greek and New Testament at a Mennonite Seminary for over 20 years. Relaxed and efficient discussion of each event. Difficult passages (eg cursing of the fig tree) calmly treated by reviews of other expositors with sane conclusions. 437 pages with bibliography, £5.10, TB £3.95.

Mark St AP
John Calvin

See "A Harmony of the Gospels" above.

Commentary on Mark Kregel
H B Swete

The Greek text with notes. W&H text used with Swete's discussion. Of value only to those studying the Greek text. 554 pages, cloth, £6.95, TB £6.30.

"The Gospel According to Mark" by J A Alexander (1881) is a fine commentary, reprinted by Banner of Truth (1960) and well worth watching for second-hand.

Luke

Luke   BT
William Hendriksen

The long awaited commentary on Luke's Gospel has taken Dr Hendriksen over 3 years to write and will be over 1200 pages long. It follows the author's usual style except that additional practical lessons are added to each section. An article is included on the interpretation of parables. The Baker volume has been announced in the USA for October 1978 and we look forward to the English edition from Banner in 1979. Cloth, no UK price details to hand.

Expository Thoughts on the Gospels   Baker/EP
J C Ryle

Luke is Volume 2 of the 4 volume paperback series issued by Baker in the USA and imprinted in England by Evangelical Press. Ryle's style is unchanging, but the three lessons he draws on each event or parable are always first class. He maintains a warm, simple, yet vital level of application. Ryle barely attempts a serious exposition, but in selecting what he sees as leading lessons he sets an example in communication. The Luke volume, paper, £3.75.

Luke   St AP
John Calvin

See "Harmony of the Gospels" above.

Lange Commentaries — Luke   Zondervan
Prof J J Von Oosterzee

The commentary on Luke is exceptionally good with large sections devoted to homiletic suggestions. (See under Whole Bible.)

Notes

The works listed earlier on miracles and parables should, of course, be consulted and used as commentaries on large portions of Luke. These works are usually more suggestive than formal verse-by-verse commentaries.

R C H Lenski's "Interpretation of St Luke's Gospel" (Augsburg) has only just gone out of print. Another large work full of helpful exegesis and information and worth looking for.

The "Suggestive Homiletic Commentary on the New Testament" edited by W H Van Doren, has two volumes devoted to Luke. These are often seen second-hand and for preachers who can learn to use them are most helpful. "Well named 'suggestive'," said Spurgeon, "It teems and swarms with homiletic hints." There is hope that these volumes will be reprinted in 1979 in the USA.

The NIC series commentary on Luke by the South African pastor Norval Geldenhuys has been seen described as the best available. (It just goes to show that different methods of assessment are employed in the evaluation of commentaries!) Geldenhuys includes much good word-study kind of comment together with useful (and original) scholarly footnotes and asides. But the general standard of comment is lacking as far as spiritual application is concerned. If one is preaching or teaching through the Gospel of Luke such a commentary will contribute little to warm, applied material. Its expense (nearly £8) hardly justifies its modest usefulness.

Sir Wm Ramsay's "Luke the Physician" is being reprinted in 1979. It is hard to understand why two American Reformed publishing houses have suddenly taken a liking for Ramsay's old volumes. They are full of historical and geographical background material — masses of it. Enough of this kind of help is already in much better works. Sir William contributes nothing spiritual.

John

Exposition of Gospel of John   Zondervan
A W Pink

Pink at his best. This highly 'experimental', warm commentary will furnish real help and will encourage considerable application. Much better than Hendriksen at this. 4 volumes complete in 1 volume, cloth, £10.50, TB £8.50.

John   BT
William Hendriksen

This commentary is so good that the preacher will require nothing more to satisfy word study, technical and doctrinal requirements. It is also good for stimulating application to believers. All that is left to be done by others is further experimental application, and especially application of passages to unbelievers in evangelistic messages. (Pink is vital, with Spurgeon and Taylor on Miracles). 2 vols in one, 250+507 pages, cloth, £4.50.

Gospel According to John
John Calvin

St A P

The Torrance modern translation edition. Volume I is John 1-10 (278 pages); Volume II is John 11-21 and 1 John (315 pages). Preachers really should have Calvin. Cloth £3.50 each.

Expository Thoughts on the Gospels
J C Ryle

Baker/EP

See comment under Luke. The section on John is volumes 3 and 4 in the Baker paperback series imprinted here by Evangelical Press. Once again J C Ryle selects the essential points and applies them to the heart. For preachers, Pink easily comes first, but Ryle always contributes something. The 2 volumes, paper, £5.95.

Our Lord Prays for His Own
M Rainsford

Moody

This famous exposition is not so well known these days. It is an exceedingly warm preaching of John 17. Unusual because this 19th century London preacher sets aside, for the purpose of this work, all practical considerations and deals with the prayer solely to lift out the great spiritual facts. It is 476 pages of what used to be called "elevated spiritual thought". As a spiritual refresher it is magnificent and is a source of stimulation for preachers with original material. 476 pages, paper, £5.10, TB £3.75.

Notes

Van Doren also issued the "Suggestive Commentary on John in 2 volumes." About this Spurgeon makes his well known comment, "If men who read this volume do not preach the better for so doing, it is not Mr Van Doren's fault; they must be Van Dolts by nature." This remarkable volume packed with suggestive notes may also (like the Luke volumes) be reprinted in 1979 in USA. In the meantime some second-hand volumes still present themselves.

Though R C H Lenski's great work, "The Interpretation of St John" is now out of print in UK, if found it is a solid investment.

Fredk L Godet's big commentary on John is being reprinted by Kregel in 1979 and will cost about £10, though whether Godet will add much to the above range of available works is doubtful.

Banner of Truth reprinted the fine Exposition of John by the Puritan George Hutcheson. Though no longer in print, unsold copies may still be seen in bookshops (or second-hand).

All the modern "mini" commentaries (Everyman's Tyndale etc) are skimpy and poor on the Gospels. One can safely say they are simply never worth consulting.

Paul:Life&Work

Life & Epistles of St Paul
W J Conybeare & J S Howson

Eerdmans

"Far superior to any other work on the subject. It stands like some o'ertopping alp, a marvel among Scriptural biographies." (CHS). Today it remains THE standard work on Paul. "All other books on Paul must take second place." (Wilbur Smith). This great book traces the life of Paul with more detail than any other. It is, effectively, a commentary on much of Acts. The comments on Paul's epistles are very general, but the main part of this work has still never been approached for quality and usefulness. 850 pages, cloth, £4.85, TB £4.25.

Harmony of the Life of St Paul
F J Goodwin

Baker

This work is of such value to preachers it should be much more widely known in Britain. Reprinted many times in the USA it is a parallel-column type harmony of the life and journeys of the Apostle — arranging relating comments from epistles next to the Acts narrative. But the esteemed author goes much further. He distils the views of Conybeare, Howson, Lightfoot and others to give the best available notes on dates and times. He includes maps and very clear treatments of all the controversial elements of the apostle's life. For preaching or studying Paul this soundly evangelical work is a great aid. 240 pages, cloth, £4.30, TB £3.30.

The Life of St Paul
J Stalker

T & T Clark

"Surpassingly excellent . . . Dr Stalker gives a masterly miniature, and thousands will see more of Paul in ·it than in the life-sized portraits." (C H Spurgeon). This reprint is very cheaply produced in thin paper cover but still gives value as it is the genuine Stalker inside. 150 pages, paper, 80p.

Gleanings from Paul
A W Pink

Moody

Pink on the prayers of the apostle. An unusual, refreshing and suggestive book in the author's usual style. 360 pages, cloth, £4.40, TB £3.40.

Life and Journeys of Paul
C F Ball

Moody

A modern, popular survey of the apostle's life and journeys by an

Commentaries — Paul

89

American Presbyterian minister. A bit too much like a "story-book", but conveys a good impression, more for general readers than preachers. 253 pages, paper, £2.20, TB £1.85.

Acts

The Acts
John Calvin
St AP

Two volumes of Torrance modern translation. Once again Calvin, the forerunner of post-Reformation commentators, is still unsurpassed. He is always so unaffected and easy to follow, yet never fails to reveal and explain the sense of the passage. Volume 1, Acts 1—13 (397 pages); Vol 2, Acts 14—28 (315 pages); Cloth, £3.50 each.

Acts of the Apostles
Horatio Hackett
Judson

This was the finest work of a noted nineteenth century American Baptist seminary professor. It is a detailed verse-by-verse exposition. Full of pithy observations. This Judson Press edition is from an 1882 edition which had been revised and enlarged by Hackett. There are added notes by Alvah Hovey. (This is rather bigger than the 1872 English Bunyan Library edition in 2 volumes, which is a rare book occasionally seen at very high prices.) Not much application, but Hackett's forthright style is just suited to "bringing out" the text of Acts. This great work will appear in UK January 1979.

Studies In Acts (The Church In The House)
William Arnot
Kregel

"Intended to be read in families on Sabbath afternoons, but all who are acquainted with Dr Arnot will know that even his simplest expositions are rich and full. He hath dust of gold." — Spurgeon. In the homely, elementary, and old fashioned homilies of this work lies a wealth of suggested application for the preacher who is sensitive and watching. 560 pages, cloth, £6.80, TB £5.20.

The Acts of the Apostles
G Campbell Morgan
P&I

Campbell Morgan is not usually regarded as a Reformed exegete and many of his commentaries are diffuse and somewhat superficial. But this is a real contribution to commentaries on Acts and is full of pastoral application. It is Dr Campbell Morgan at his very best. 432 pages, paper, £1.80.

The Acts of the Apostles   **Baker**
Richard Rackham

Rackham upholds baptismal regeneration and a positively Romish view of church officers, etc. Because of the absence of evangelical light and experimental or homiletical usefulness the work is listed reluctantly. It is here only for its technical contribution as a subsidiary commentary. (Klock do an expensive version (£8.50) which places the work right out of court. Non-evangelical items are never worth that much). Originally part of the "Westminster Commentaries", 1901. 524 pages, paper, £5.40, TB £4.30.

Notes

Lenski is invaluable on Acts. Once again this Augsburg commentary has only just gone out of print and copies should be around second-hand.

John Kitto's Daily Bible Illustrations, though over a century old, still turn up in second-hand shops. The volume on "The Apostles and the Early Church" is really good.

Principal Thomas Lindsay's "The Church and the Ministry in the Early Centuries" was reprinted in 1977 by Klock and Klock. It is a grand old work by the Free Church of Scotland professor, but it can still be procured easily second-hand. In any case it will be worth waiting for a very much cheaper paperback version due in from another USA publisher early in 1979.

J A Alexander's commentary, "The Acts of the Apostles" (1869) was once reprinted by Banner of Truth. Now out of print again, it is a full and concise commentary worth seeking second-hand.

Macauley's Expository Commentary on Acts (once from Eerdmans) has been reissued by Moody, but it is a long way from being expository, and not worth much to preachers.

F F Bruce continues in print on Acts with very little to say on the message of the word. His most recent work, "Paul, Apostle of the Free Spirit" (Paternoster) betrays the author's neo-liberal view of the inspiration and infallibility of Scripture more clearly than ever. It lacks the true evangelical spirit and the depth of the older works recommended above.

Some authors, especially Dr Stalker and Conybeare/Howson, take the view that the early Christians continued to worship in the Temple, and only became separately constituted for worship when persecution and dispersion drove them out. (This idea is seized upon today by ecumenically minded evangelicals to justify their continuation in dead denominational situations). While we respect and recommend the authors just named as the very best on Paul, we must register complete disagreement with these "establishment principle" views. Our Saviour planned in eternity to establish a separated, spiritual church in the New Testament. The Holy Spirit gave notice of it in the Old Testament (Jer 31.31 etc); the Saviour taught the disciples about it and prepared them for it through the great church metaphors and numerous plain statements separating the disciples from Judaism; Pentecost signalled the rule of the Holy Spirit over the separated entity; the provision of apostles demonstrated an organisation definitely and defiantly independent of Judaism; the early profession of obedience to God rather than men indicated their total lack of allegiance to the Jewish rule, and so on. To prove that the young church members went to the Temple for witness and not as worshippers within Judaism is so easy that the pages would run away with us.

Epistles: General

Expositions of St Paul's Epistles   BT
Richard Sibbes

This volume includes various expositions from Philippians by an outstanding Puritan. Pages 6-193 contain a selection of choice, readable and highly applied discourses, including great addresses on "The Providence of God" (Phil 2.24); a 97 page exposition of Phil 3; a sermon on "The Redemption of Bodies" (Phil 3.21) and one on "The Art of Contentment" (Phil 4.11-13). Pages 225-256 carry expository sermons on texts from Romans, including "The Privileges of the Faithful" (Rom 8.28). Other discourses are included from Galatians, Ephesians and 1 Timothy. It should be noted that these are sermons on just a few verses. It would be disastrous for preachers to imitate these long, over stocked addresses in our modern situation. But to study the amount of illustration and close application in these messages will surely convict us of the inadequacy of our efforts and catalyse real experimental preaching. 540 pages, cloth, £4.00.

Exposition of the Epistles   BT
James Ferguson

Exposition of the Epistles to the Galatians, Ephesians, Philippians, Colossians and Thessalonians, first issued 1659. A new printing of this Puritan work is to be warmly welcomed. Every verse is given almost a page, and every comment has a long section neaded "Doctrines" with four to ten doctrinal or practical points drawn from the verse. Just what all commentaries should be. This Banner volume includes David Dickson's "Short Explanation of

Hebrews", which is rich but rather brief. 582 large format pages, cloth, £6.50.

Notes

The apparent shortage of works in this section is due entirely to the abundance available specifically on each Epistle.

Romans

Commentary on Romans Kregel
W S Plumer

Dr Plumer (1802-1880) was an early Princeton graduate who became a greatly used preacher and Seminary professor in the USA. In this commentary (issued 1867) he collects material from everyone else so his work reflects all the great divines up to that time. He includes considerable additional information about the apostle Paul. Plumer's commentary is easily the best on Romans in terms of suggestion to preachers for it is packed with practical application. Every now and then he actually falls to preaching such as in Rom 8, "Are you a child of sorrow? Are you perplexed? Are you cast down? Verse 28 covers all your case...". Every chapter is concluded with long strings of numbered doctrinal and practical remarks. Truly this is a preachers' commentary. 646 pages, cloth, £5.40, TB £4.35.

Romans BT or Eerdmans
Charles Hodge

Hodge compresses so much into all his commentaries, and yet always remains clear and understandable. He was a prince among Reformed theologians. Banner of Truth have a nice cloth edition at £3.00, and a sturdy paperback alternative comes from Eerdmans. There is not much application in Hodge, but his handling of technical and doctrinal matter is unsurpassed. Hodge was Professor of Biblical Literature and later of Theology at Princeton Seminary from 1820 to 1878. (His son, A A Hodge, succeeded him). Eerdmans edn: 458 pages, £2.45, TB £1.95.

Epistles to the Romans St AP
John Calvin

This volume includes 1 & 2 Thessalonians. In the Torrance series. Calvin is essential reading through these epistles — and as usual his flowing prose (especially in this new translation) makes him the easiest to follow as he unfolds the arguments of Romans. 423 pages, cloth, £3.50.

Studies in Romans   Kregel
H C G Moule

For this volume Moule adopts such a pleasant style that he is
easily underestimated. He frequently says in a sentence what
others say in several paragraphs. The tone is warm throughout and
there is good application. An excellent makeweight commentary.
270 pages, kivar, £1.90, TB £1.65.

Romans   BT
Geoffrey Wilson

Subtitled "A Digest of Reformed Comment" this modern commentary says much in its brief verse-by-verse comments. There are
numerous quotations from Reformed preachers and commentators
of the past. It can safely be said that most modern works, once the
word definitions are set aside, do not contain a fraction of the
spiritual thought and application to be found in these Wilson
'digests'. A good second commentary. 254 pages, paper, £1.25.
(Other similar commentaries by this author have been published on
1 & 2 Cor, Gal, Eph, 1 & 2 Thess and Hebrews).

Commentary on Romans   Kregel
Martin Luther

A great classic. Perhaps every preacher should have at least this
commentary by Luther. He loved this epistle, and his unique and
distinctive style is most effective here. 223 pages, paper, £2.45, TB
£1.90.

Romans in the Greek New Testament   Eerdmans
Kenneth Wuest

It is far better to have the work of a specialist in word studies,
than to buy a modern Tyndale/IVP type of commentary which
does the same job much less effectively in order to give space to
other background and spiritual comment. (Which they do badly as
well). These "fall-between-two-stools" efforts are also painfully
expensive. This volume will prove a great boon in preparation
whether a preacher is an able NT Greek scholar or not. (It is
intended for students with no such knowledge). See remarks under
Mark. Paper, £2.10, TB £1.60.

Notes

*"A Suggestive Commentary on St Paul's Epistle to the Romans"
by Thomas Robinson (2 vols — 1871 etc) is still seen second-hand.
In the Van Doren series, it is two whole books of single-sentence
comments and preaching suggestions.*
W G T Shedd's "A Critical and Doctrinal Commentary on

Commentaries — Romans

... Romans" is back in print from Klock and Klock for around £7.00. Originals (1879, etc) and Zondervan reprints (1960s) of this still turn up. Baker plan a paper issue in 1979. About £3.00.

R C H Lenski's "The Interpretation of . . . Romans" (Augsburg) is only just out of print. A very large commentary, it is very valuable.

Robert Haldane's commentary on Romans has warm application and is still in print, though we think Plumer does the same style of work very much better and without Haldane's complex polemical digressions. (Haldane in cloth, TB £3.95).

John Murray's Commentary on Romans is still available (New International — Eerdmans) at around £6 — but his style here is so very involved that it is unlikely to be studied much, or to inspire preaching.

F L Godet, the noted Swiss Protestant theologian compiled a great commentary on the Greek text of Romans which has been reprinted by Kregel (544 pages, £7). We feel it is too technical and heavy to include in the listing. It is more of a library work.

Corinthians

I & II Corinthians   **BT**
Charles Hodge

This very full commentary is a basic tool for preachers. Hodge follows his usual remarkably economical, lucid style. For all round excellence there is nothing modern to compare with Hodge, though we are left needing more experimental provocation. First published 1868/9. Spurgeon said, "The more we use Hodge, the more we value him." 690 pages, cloth, £3.50.

Epistles to the Corinthians   **St AP**
John Calvin

These volumes are further examples of Calvin's genius. (The church discipline sections are of very great importance to pastors). Perhaps other men can be excused for not being so profound, but they could try to be as clear. Calvin never makes any attempt at adding applications to his comments. But he has little need to, for his style manages to imply obvious application all the time. In this he is a rare commentator, but must be read with expectation and respect. Many a man has been heard to assert that Calvin never gave him anything practical. Such friends are telling us more about themselves than they are about Calvin. It is no exaggeration to say that nearly every sentence of Calvin in some chapters could be a heading for a point in a sermon. Volume 1, I Corinthians, 370 pages; Volume 2, 2 Corinthians and Timothy, Titus & Philemon, 401 pages; cloth, £3.50 each.

Called to Be Saints   Baker
R G Gromacki

This exposition of I Corinthians divides the book up in a refreshingly practical and logical way. It includes much background information and is extremely readable. This will be appreciated by preachers as a great stimulation to warm and practical preaching through the book. By the present Professor of NT Greek at Cedarville College, Ohio. 209 pages, paper, £2.40, TB £1.85.

Commentary on I Corinthians   Kregel
F L Godet

Prof Godet was best known for his works on Luke and this epistle. A great Swiss Protestant scholar (1812-1900), Godet has here provided the largest evangelical exposition (reprinted from the T & T Clark edition). If the R C H Lenski volume on 1 & 2 Cor had still been in print, it is doubtful whether the Godet classic would have been listed here, but in the absence of Lenski the older work comes back to the forefront as the leading 'heavyweight'. Full of exegetical help; very technical, yet endowed with practical comment. 928 pages, cloth, £7.95, TB £7.45.

Stand Firm in the Faith   Baker
Robert G Gromacki

An expoisition of 2 Corinthians of the same quality as the author's "Called to be Saints". A refreshing and unusual dividing up of the book which has an emphasis on challenging the individual to self examination. 160 pages, paper, £2.45, TB £1.85.

2nd Epistle to the Corinthians   P & I
H C G Moule

Another exposition by Moule worthy of inclusion on the Corinthians shelf. Moule was weak in some areas of doctrine but this is a good "second" commentary with suggested themes and application. 165 pages, paper, £1.70.

II Corinthians   Kregel
Albert Barnes

We think Barnes is seen at his best in all the epistles. His mastery of brevity should not be despised. After a short explanatory comment on each phrase, he is all application. In addition there are frequent sections headed "Remarks" which contain even more personal and practical application. We would much sooner have this old work than Hughes (see below) on this epistle. (See "Barnes' Notes on the New Testament" under New Testament, General).

Paul's Second Epistle to the Corinthians   Eerdmans
P E Hughes

This NIC work is more substantial than most in the series. It is heavily technical and exegetical rather than homiletical as the author admits in his preface. It is the most scholarly evangelical technical work available on II Cor, though the source bibliography shows alarming omissions. For anyone requiring a coldly objective treatment, this is to be recommended, but it is devoid of the slightest application and stimulation for preachers. The man who can use such a commentary often would need a pretty hard constitution. 508 pages, cloth, £6.70.

Notes

From the reference to R C H Lenski above the recommendation of second-hand volumes of Lenski follows inevitably. Augsburg really should have left this 1341 page volume in print. First issued by American Lutheran in 1937, it is a solid and important commentary which has seen numerous editions over 40 years.

R S Candlish's great exposition of 1 Cor 15, "Life in a Risen Saviour" has been reprinted by James & Klock (USA) and is available, cloth, £6.50, (EP) TB £4.50.

New International (Eerdmans) has F W Grosheide on I Corinthians. This is useful but scanty, and very poor on some key passages (such as the discipline procedure of I Cor 5). It also has a complex literary structure for such a light commentary.

Galatians

Galatians   BT
William Hendriksen

See previous comments on Dr Hendriksen's commentary on John. This is the best modern commentary combining doctrine, word studies (though these are not so full as to eliminate Wuest); tracing through of themes and arguments; background information and a reasonable amount of application. 260 pages, cloth, £2.50.

Epistle to the Galatians   St AP
John Calvin

This Torrance series (new translation) volume includes Ephesians,

Philippians and Colossians. All that was said under "Corinthians" applies here. In places every line of Calvin could be a heading in a message. 369 pages, cloth, £3.50.

Machen's Notes on Galatians
P & R
J Gresham Machen

From the very opening of this work it is clearly the product of a scholar of the greatest stature. Even the greeting is expounded with originality and charm. Prof Gresham Machen joined the renowned Princeton faculty in 1906. When in 1926 liberal influence took over, Prof Machen (with Robert Dick Wilson, Oswald Allis, Van Til and others) founded Westminster Theological Seminary. He was the principal defender of the old faith through those terrible events. This is the only commentary which really deals adequately with "the peril of inconsistency" (Gal 2.11 etc). Dr Machen must be studied; his comments are unique. Technical word comments are made in a very popular style with unusual illustrations and explanations. 234 pages, paper, £2.50, TB £1.85.

Galatians in the Greek New Testament
Eerdmans
Kenneth Wuest

More detailed word studies of the key words in each verse bringing to the reader lacking a knowledge of Greek a clearer meaning of the original words. See previous comments under "Mark" and "Romans". But Greek readers will certainly value it too. 190 pages, paper, £1.80, TB £1.10.

Commentary on Galatians
Zondervan
J B Lightfoot

Bishop Lightfoot was for years Professor of Divinity at Cambridge. This is the standard scholarly commentary on the Greek text of Galatians. Verse by verse study (which is very technical) scattered with long notes on various problems. Not spiritually applied, but not dry either for such a work. Includes dissertations. "The Brethren of the Lord" and the 82-page "Paul and the Three" are most important. 384 pages, cloth, £6.50, TB £4.75.

The Epistle to the Galatians
Eerdmans
Herman Ridderbos

Though padded out by large print and line gaps giving much less material than expected, this is a better commentary than most in the New International series. Ridderbos has a lively way of unravelling the difficult reasoning. 238 pages, cloth, £4.60, TB £3.15.

Commentary on Galatians   Kregel
Martin Luther

A fine new reprint of this classic. "I prefer this book of Martin Luther's (except the Bible) before all the books I have ever seen, as most fit for a wounded conscience." — Bunyan. (This edition includes the Life of Luther.) Cloth, £6.80, TB £5.10.

Notes

"Interpretation of Galatians, Ephesians and Philippians" by R C H Lenski (Augsburg) is a fine modern commentary just out of print. From an Evangelical Lutheran scholar it is mainly technical with some warm spiritual comment.

The "Historical Commentary on Galatians" by Sir Wm Ramsay is being reprinted by both Baker and Klock. Previous comment under Luke applies. All we need to know of ancient background is in better works where background is kept in the background. An expensive overabundance of this kind of thing will not assist spiritual preaching.

Ephesians

Ephesians   BT
William Hendriksen

Please see previous comments. In this commentary Dr Hendriksen maintains his exceptional standard, and through chapters 4 and 5 yields to a highly applicatory style. 290 pages, cloth, £3.00.

Commentary on Ephesians   St AP
John Calvin

This is part of the Galatians volume (see Galatians entry).

Commentary on Ephesians   Zondervan
John Eadie

A highly technical, scholarly commentary with much discussion of the Greek text, but with a warmer evangelical style than Lightfoot. Prof Eadie (1810-1872) was a Scottish minister who seceded at the Disruption with the Bonars and became a professor at the United Presbyterian College. This is a truly painstaking work. 492 pages, cloth, £9.50, TB £7.25.

Ephesians and Colossians   Eerdmans
Kenneth Wuest

See previous entries. These word studies will greatly assist a preacher whether he handles NT Greek for himself or not. Paper, £1.70, TB £1.35.

Ephesian Studies   Kregel
H C G Moule

A much more devotional work, trite in places and suggestive in others. A useful companion to one of the more profound expositions. 176 pages, paper, £1.70, TB £1.45.

Sermons on Ephesians   BT
John Calvin

These sermons were first issued in an English translation in 1577. Today they are as special as ever. Cloth, £4.50.

Notes

Charles Hodge on Ephesians is nearly 400 pages of exceptional technical and applied comment. Banner once reprinted the 1856 American edition which may possibly be obtained second-hand.

B F Westcott's commentary on Ephesians has been reprinted in the USA and is seen offered by Reformed distributors. An Anglo-Catholic-cum-liberal scholar, his work is highly technical and his theological treatment poor.

J Armitage Robinson is also in print again at about £8.00 but is too technical (especially as we have Eadie) to be recommended.

Philippians

Philippians   BT
William Hendriksen

See previous comments. Dr Hendriksen is a good guide through the relationships and conduct passages of this epistle. The best modern work. 218 pages, cloth, £3.00.

Commentary on Philippians   St AP
John Calvin

This is (with Ephesians and Colossians) bound in the Galatians volume.

Lectures on the Book of Philippians   Klock
Robert Johnstone

A great commentary from the nineteenth century Edinburgh scholar and preacher. Derived from preached material, this exposition has a very strong practical content which lifts it above many other commentaries. "A noble volume. A real boon to the man who purchases it." —CHS. 498 pages, cloth, £8.00, TB £6.25.

Commentary on Philippians   Zondervan
J B Lightfoot

See comment on Galatians. For over 100 years the standard work for technical exegesis. (This includes Lightfoot's Dissertation on the Christian Ministry, pages 181 to 269.) 350 pages, cloth, £6.50, TB £4.75.

Devotional Commentary on Philippians   Kregel
F B Meyer

Just what the title suggests. Full of application and in this respect it is a needed corrective to much that is called Reformed preaching. It is full of F B Meyer's rather forced and fancy divisions and headings — but beneath all this there is a lot to be gained. 264 pages, paper, £2.20, TB £1.75.

Philippians in the Greek New Testament   Eerdmans
Kenneth Wuest

See previous comments. Nearly 300 words each receive a third of a page here. 120 pages, paper, £1.40, TB £1.10.

Philippians — Triumph in Christ   Moody
John Walvoord

Dr Walvoord (President of Dallas Seminary) is more successful than most authors seem to be at making a brief commentary worthwhile. He expounds along the line of his title. There are original comments here and many parts will enthuse the preacher with the germ of an application. In the Moody "Everyman's" series; a useful subsidiary commentary. 127 pages, paper, £1.40, TB £1.05.

Studies in Philippians   Kregel
H C G Moule

Once again Moule provides a companion to other commentaries. Not as good as others by him, but still worth using. (Very small print). 134 pages, paper, £1.30, TB £1.15.

Notes

See the entry under "Epistles — General" for Richard Sibbes, "Expositions of St Paul" (BT). Pages 6-193 are devoted to discourses on Philippians.

Colossians

Colossians and Philemon   **BT**
William Hendriksen

Commentators tend to run out of material on Colossians and all but a few commentaries are lamentably short. Dr Hendriksen has provided a full length exposition. Of all the modern offerings this will be the best. The New International and IVP/Tyndale volumes provide much less material and less practical comment. 256 pages, cloth, £2.50.

Colossians   **St AP**
John Calvin

This is part of the Galatians volume. (See Galatians entry).

Commentary on Colossians and Philemon   **Zondervan**
J B Lightfoot

This is another scholarly classic in the same style as Bishop Lightfoot's other work (see previous comments under Galatians and Ephesians). It is much bigger and more technical than Hendriksen, being exegetical and not practical or suggestive. 430 pages, cloth, £6.50, TB £4.75.

Colossians in the Greek New Testament   **Eerdmans**
Kenneth Wuest

This very useful word study commentary is included in the Ephesians volume.

Colossians and Philemon Studies   **Kregel**
H C G Moule

A very useful 'second commentary' with devotional application. 192 pages, paper, £1.80, TB £1.50.

Notes

The Colossians section of "The Epistles of Paul" by James Ferguson (BT) has much stimulating application. (See entry under Epistles, General).

If anyone happens to be searching for Dr R C H Lenski's commentary on the Pastoral Epistles (just out of print with Augsburg) Colossians is bound in the same volume.

Barnes is good on Ephsians-Philippians-Colossians, always giving extra explanation of controversial points. See entry under New Testament, General.

Thessalonians

I & II Thessalonians   BT
William Hendriksen

See previous comments. (It is especially reassuring to have Dr Hendriksen's sane treatment of eschatological passages, especially the 'man of sin' in II Thessalonians 2). 214 pages, cloth, £2.50.

I & II Thessalonians   St AP
John Calvin

See Romans — these epistles are included in the Romans volume of the Torrance new translation edition. Rich exposition, yet clearer to follow than anyone else! 433 pages, cloth, £3.50.

I & II Thessalonians   BT
Geoffrey Wilson

See previous comment under Romans. 124 pages, paper, 60p.

Lange's Commentary   Zondervan

I & II Thessalonians are by Dr C Amberlen and Dr C J Riggenbach, translated with many additions by Dr John Lillie. The homiletical and practical notes are very fine. Dy Lillie's additions include quotations from the other leading commentators. (See under Lange — Whole Bible).

Notes

Once again, many applications and doctrinal observations are made for each verse of both these epistles in James Ferguson's "The Epistles of Paul". (See under Epistles, General.)

R C H Lenski, like Dr Hendriksen, excels in the eschatological and 'man of sin' passages. His I & II Thessalonians commentary is part of "An Interpretation of the Epistles to the Colossians, Thessalonians, Timothy, Titus and Philemon" published from 1937-77 by Augsburg, but now withdrawn.

Timothy, Titus

Timothy & Titus   BT
William Hendriksen

See previous comments. Dr Hendriksen is very good with officers,   **103** their duties, church order etc. He does full justice to these practical epistles, 404 pages, cloth, £3.00.

The Pastoral Epistles   Moody
Homer Kent

A solid 320 page exposition. Tends towards a word-study type of commentary and is very faithful and clear. Includes valuable and original thought. Will definitely add to the material in Dr Hendriksen's commentary as the pastoral passages (especially relating to officers, order, widows etc) are extremely well worked out. Of real worth to pastors. Dr Kent is President of Grace Theological Seminary, Winona Lake. 320 pages, cloth, £3.75, TB £2.95.

I & II Timothy & Titus   St AP
John Calvin

Included in the volume for II Corinthians.

The Pastoral Epistles   Eerdmans
K S Wuest

The usual arrangement from Dr Wuest. Expanded translations and word studies. Again, very useful work. Why are these brief word studies so underestimated today? See previous comments. Particularly valuable on the Pastorals where detailed study of terms is so important. 209 pages, paper, £1.80, TB £1.10.

Notes

The outstanding work on the Pastoral Epistles by Patrick Fairbairn is still sometimes seen second-hand either in its 1874-1898 printings, or in the Zondervan 1956 reprint. There are some hopes for a reissue. The notes and comments here stand in a class of their own. Some copies of the delisted Klock reprint can still be found.

H. P Lidden's "Explanatory Analysis" of I Timothy is coming back in the USA, but be warned: it is a terribly technical, dry analysis of the Greek text.

R C H Lenski's "Interpretation of Colossians, Thessalonians, Timothy, Titus and Philemon" gives 475 pages to the Pastorals and contains much valuable reasoning. (Augsburg 1937-77, withdrawn).

For study of the Pastorals, W E Vine's "Expository Dictionary of New Testament Words" is particularly useful (see Reading List entry under New Testament).

Philemon

Commentaries on Philemon are, because of the shortness of the epistle, generally appended to other works.

John Calvin: see 2nd Corinthians volume in the Torrance edition.
William Hendriksen: see Colossians and Philemon.
H C G Moule: see Colossians and Philemon Studies.
J C Lightfoot: see Commentary on Colossians and Philemon.

Hebrews

Hebrews: The Epistle of Warning   **Kregel**
John Owen

The major commentary on Hebrews. This is a radically edited version executed by a most sympathetic expert. Though hard to believe, the greatly shortened version retains all the rich argument and sense of the expository parts of the 7-volume original work. With such a paperback available, it simply makes no sense for preachers NOT to have Owen on Hebrews. Every few verses of commentary are punctuated by Owen's numerous "observations" which are doctrinal and practical. These, with the typical Owen| illustrations, are unmatched for preachers. 283 pages, paper, £2.45, TB £1.90.

While it is a great asset to have the abridged Owen listed above, the original 7 volume Goold edition (1855) is still seen from time to time secondhand, or alternatively the American NFCE reprint of 1960. The abridgement is, for ordinary purposes, more usable, but the original includes very important treatment of many subjects. In the compiler's view the most significant reasoning ever published on the Covenant, and the case for Sinai as a kind of re-iteration of the Covenant of Works (as held by historic Calvinistic Independents) is found here in a treatise attached to the comments on Hebrews 8.

Hebrews   **Baker**
A W Pink

This is a very large commentary, but Pink has contributed it in a much needed area. It includes the riches of the past, for Pink takes account of the great expositors, and it is highly experimental and suggestive. Undoubtedly the most useful commentary in print on Hebrews. Owen is unique; Wuest is useful technically; Lenski an example of detailed technical help; Brown is full of solid doctrine — but for real application Pink holds the field. Over 1300 pages, cloth, £11.50, TB £8.75.

Epistle . . . to the Hebrews and I & II Peter   St AP
John Calvin

The Torrance edition. This portion of Calvin is precious. See previous comments. 378 pages, cloth, £3.50.

Hebrews   BT
John Brown

This great commentary is strongly recommended both for its technical exegesis and its doctrinal applications.Longwinded and lofty in tone but invaluable. Will not inspire preaching quite like Pink, but will give a safe exegetical anchor. 728 pages, cloth, £3.50.

Hebrews   Eerdmans
K S Wuest

Dr Wuest's method is very appropriate for Hebrews. These careful, extended notes on the key words of each verse will suggest much to the minds of preachers. Where Dr Wuest strays into commentary writing he is not so good. His notes on Hebrews 6, for example, are rather poor, but the word definitions are very valuable. 271 pages, paper, £1.80, TB £1.45.

Notes

If a modern heavier work is still required providing full textual reasoning, then R C H Lenski is the best, (Interpretation of Hebrews and James, Augsburg) but he must be procured second-hand.

The greatest commentary of all on Hebrews is that by William Goudge in 3 large volumes. If all commentaries were like it, the general standard of preaching would be much higher. It is impossible to describe the notes and hints listed out from every verse. It is very, very rare.

Eerdmans have a new work by P E Hughes but it has all the drawbacks of being much too dry and exegetical. We have all the technical help we need in John Brown; a mass of warm application in Pink; and the jewels of edited Owen. If the price of this work (nearly £10) hindered a preacher from securing the others, he would be the poorer for it.

The Cobbin's edition of Notes on Hebrews by Albert Barnes has 401 pages. This shows the length of this material, which is found in the Kregel 1-volume Barnes (see New Testament, General).

James

James   **BT**
Robert Johnstone

Another work by the distinguished Edinburgh preacher (see Philippians). First published 1871 this work gained an honorary DD from the University of Edinburgh. It is derived from sermons and is very readable and strongly applied. An uncharacteristic defect is the absurdly sacramental significance attached to the annointing of James 5.14. 444 pages, cloth, £3.50.

James   **St AP**
John Calvin

In the Torrance edition "A Harmony of the Gospels" Vol III includes the Epistles of James and Jude. 60 pages apply to James. (See New Testament, General).

Barnes' Notes   **Kregel**
Albert Barnes

In the one-volume edition of "Barnes' Notes on the New Testament" there is a good section on James with some unusual condensed comment, and interesting notes under the heading, "Reconciliation of Paul and James" (see New Testament, General.)

Lange's Commentary   **Zondervan**

The commentary on James is in the James to Revelation volume and is by Prof J P Lange and Prof J J Von Oosterzee. The exegetical and homiletical comments are first class. James is covered in 148 pages. (See Whole Bible).

James, Faith in Action   **Moody**
G Coleman Luck

This "Everyman's" series volume suffers heavily from the light, modern American approach but has some good comment. Where commentaries are few, it is useful as a makeweight. 128 pages, paper, £1.40, TB £1.05.

Notes

"Epistle of James" by Joseph Mayor is another work which Baker and Klock are competing over. The author was not evangelical in outlook and this commentary is as technical as it could possibly be. Why do the Reformed reprinters sometimes

scramble over such unspiritual heavy works when there are so many really stimulating works waiting to be reprinted?

Thomas Manton's commentary on James used to be in print with Banner of Truth. Though very old fashioned it is full of good things and well worth finding second-hand. Equal space is given to exposition and 'observations' of a doctrinal and applied nature.

The exposition of James by R C H Lenski is included in the same volume as Hebrews by this author. It is technically very thorough and is particularly good on personal conduct passages. (Augsburg, out of print).

Earl Kelly's "James, A primer for Christian Living" (Presbyterian & Reformed) has been reviewed, but we think it represents a level of work which really ought to be surpassed by any preacher.

Peter

The First Epistle of Peter   BT
John Brown

This is not a verse-by-verse commentary but one which takes themes (as Calvin does, though at much greater length). The work is highly exhortational and applied, thus encouraging closely experimental preaching. 2 vols, cloth, the set £6.00.

Commentary on First Peter   Kregel
Robert Leighton

No commentary has ever been praised as highly as this for its spirit of reverence and fervour. It was of Leighton's works that Dr Mills wrote the oft-quoted lines, "There is a spirit in them I never met with in any other human writings, nor can I read many lines in them without being moved." Kregel are to be commended for this fine edition of "The immortal work of Archbishop Leighton" (Schaff). 500 pages, cloth, £6.75, TB £4.95.

I & II Peter   St AP
John Calvin

Included with the Hebrews volume in the Torrance series.

Lectures on I & II Peter   Klock
John Lillie

A real classic this full and satisfying exposition is far more worthwhile than any modern offerings. More technical and less applied than Brown, but both epistles are covered. 550 pages, cloth, £8.80, TB £6.75.

First Peter   Eerdmans
Kenneth Wuest

See previous comments on Dr Wuest's studies. A useful companion
to larger works. Paper, £1.20, TB 95p.

The Epistle of First Peter   James Family
Robert Johnstone

All the usual merits of this author's work is here. We rate it behind
Brown, Leighton and Lillie but Johnston adherents may disagree.
Cloth, £7.20, TB £5.40.

Notes

*The remaining 'moderns' of the NIC and Tyndale series cannot
even approach the above works and are therefore not worth
listing.*

Epistles of John

The Epistles of John   Moody
D W Burdick

Dr Burdick's work on tongues has already been recommended as
one of the best available treatments of the subject. Up to the same
mark is this analysis and summary of John's epistles. The difficult
passages are handled well. 127 pages, paper £1.40, TB £1.05.

Epistles of John   St AP
John Calvin

These are included in Vol II of "The Gospel According to St
John" in the Torrance Edition. Calvin is supreme in expounding
the problem passages.

Fellowship in the Life Eternal   James & Klock
George G Findlay

First issued in 1909 this is an important work with a careful kind
of style. Though strange in parts it is the biggest work in print
suitable for preachers (originally part of the Expositor's Bible
series). Cloth, £7.00, TB £4.95.

Notes

*We desperately need in print some of the experimental works
on these epistles and there is no shortage of candidates. Robert
Candlish on 1 John (from 1870) was reprinted by the Banner of
Truth but is not coming back. What a superb commentary! Even*

better for preachers is the abundance of example found in Hugh Binning's "Fellowship with God", a Puritan reprinted from 1833 by the RTS. James Morgan of Belfast issued in 1866 an "Exposition of 1 John" full of application and first class comment. Then the wonderful exposition by John Stock (1865 etc) — all these, or at least one of them would delight preachers.

Baker are reprinting "The Tests of Life" by Robert Law (first issued 1909) which is an unusual study of 1 John. This will be the subject of a Review Sheet in 1979.

Jude

Commentary on Jude   James Family
William & Jenkyn

This Puritan work (Jenkyn lived 1617-85) was reprinted many times last century. Spurgeon's comment is perfect: "Earnest and popular, but very full and profoundly learned. A treasure-house of good things." Full of Puritan application. Cloth, £5.85, TB £4.50.

Jude, The Acts of the Apostates   Moody
S Maxwell Coder

Dr Coder has taken an original and very stimulating approach to Jude lifting this "Everyman's" volume way above the general stature of the series. The uniquely problematical passages (eg verse 9) are tackled most creditably. Preachers will value this. 127 pages, paper, £1.45, TB £1.05.

An Exposition of the Epistle of Jude   Klock
Thomas Manton

Another full and rewarding Puritan commentary (issued 1658) which appeared after the exposition by Jenkyn. Manton says that after comparing his own manuscript with Jenkyn's work he omitted or shortened anything which constituted a duplication. 375 pages, cloth, £5.60, TB £4.30.

Revelation

More Than Conquerors   Baker
William Hendriksen

Once published in the UK but now only from Baker, this is essential reading before embarking on an exposition of Revelation.

Dr Hendriksen demonstrates that Revelation consists of a series of sections each of which views the Gospel age from a different point of view. One (for example) views the way God deals with men — by the Gospel; by afflictions; by warnings, and by judgements. Another views the progress and trials of the Church. Another views the world's ungodly political aspirations. (Other sections are clearly presented). Revelation was intended to help God's people understand their situation and be able to expect and explain the thinking and events in the world. It was never meant to provide fuel for wild, prophetic speculators. Dr Hendriksen is a sure guide up its soaring peaks. 285 pages, cloth, £3.75, TB £2.65.

Behold He Cometh!   Kregel
Herman Hoeksema

Much larger than the previous work, this must be the finest thing Hoeksema ever did. Preaching the spiritual, Augustinian, amillennial view of this great book was evidently his first love. (Excellent value at its price). 726 pages, cloth, £6.10, TB £4.75.

Revelation   BT
James Beverlin Ramsey

Though only extending to chapter 11 this work is particularly rich and helpful to preachers in its subjective, spiritual, pastoral application of the letters and worship chapters. In this area it is better than other commentaries. It is much less useful than others in resolving the eschatological aspects of Revelation and contains some very 'stretched' exposition to arrive at post-millennial conclusions, especially in chapter 11. However, one hesitates to criticise a work which gives such unique help to preachers for the early chapters. (First published 1873). 518 pages, cloth, £4.00.

A Simplified Commentary on Revelation   P&R
Harry Buis

Following a similar line of interpretation as Hendriksen, Buis provides a clever outline and note-style of commentary. (Amillennial). 124 pages, paper, £1.60. TB £1.15.

Revelation — An Introduction and Commentary   Baker
Homer Hailey

This promises to be a fine contribution from a "historical background" point of view, and will be the subject of a forthcoming Review Sheet. Expected January, 1979. Those who value Dr Hailey's commentary on the Minor Prophets will be interested in this work.

Commentary on Revelation   **Kregel**
H B Swete

A classic exposition (amillennial) of the Greek text (W & H): technical and suited to students of NT Greek. 576 pages, cloth, £6.95, TB £5.95.

The Old Testament in Revelation   **Baker**
Ferrill Jenkins

A novel work tracing the use of Old Testament passages and illustrations in the Book of Revelation. Suggests a theme of exposition. 151 pages, paper, £2.45, TB £1.85.

Notes

"Letters to the Seven Churches" by Sir Wm Ramsay has been recently reprinted but it is just more and more history and archaeology. The useful facts about the seven churches are given sufficient attention in the commentaries listed.

Six systems of interpretation are used on Revelation. Two of these, the "critical" and the "allegorical" alias "idealist" approaches are taken only by liberals. The "preterist" view sees the book as describing the situation in John's day and all the prophecies as being fulfilled with the fall of Rome. (Only chapters 20-22 are seen as prediction). The "historical" view sees the book as a prophecy of all human history. Everything stands for some event from the 1st century on. Barnes is an extreme devotee of this view (which is also called the "continuist" view). The "cyclic" view is that described under "More than Conquerors". (R C H Lenski was also a master of this view). Finally, the "futurist" view ties the book in with the ideas of dispensationalists. According to this, everything from chapter 4 on is about the end of the age. The compiler declares his own attachment to the "cyclic" view (also called the "synchronous" or "topical" view) with deep respect for some of the points made by the "historical" school. All who truly know the Lord seem of one mind in feeling that these must surely be the last days. As we preach we can almost hear the words of promise, "Surely I come quickly". "Amen. Even so, come, Lord Jesus." (Rev. 22.20).

The Preacher's Library
1979

The lady pauses while the carter loads his dray. In the distance can be seen the railway embankment of the Tottenham and Hampstead Junction Railway. Harringay Park Station later renamed Harringay Stadium is just out of the picture left. The brick fields and potteries fell into disuse in the early 1900s. One of London's first Greyhound Stadiums opened on the site in 1927 to be followed by the Harringay Boxing and Ice Skating Arena in 1936. The last Greyhound meeting was held in September 1987. J. Sainsbury redeveloped the site as a large supermarket and adjacent car park, opened in 1989.

(Picture, Bruce Castle).

Williamson's Potteries, Harringay, c.1902.

The Manor House, Green Lanes, 1905

The Manor House pub seems to have been established in the early 1830s, at about the time when Seven Sisters Road was cut through from Holloway to Tottenham in 1833, with a turnpike gate at its intersection with the ancient route of Green Lanes.

The building in the picture is probably the original one with late nineteenth-century modifications: a view of the 1860s shows it with a canopied iron balcony to the first floor, forming a verandah at ground floor level. The panel on the side of the building (just to the left of the lamp post) records that 'Queen Victoria halted here ye 25th Oct. AD 1843'; the circumstances are not noted. The chimneyed building on the left of the picture, masked by one of the trams, indicates the Green Lanes entrance to the depot of North Metropolitan Tramways, whose main buildings still stand to the north of the Manor House in Seven Sisters Road (now London Buses' Leaside District headquarters). In the early 1930s plans to rebuild the pub coincided with the announcement of the Piccadilly Line extension with a station at this junction. In the ensuing redevelopment, the tramway company gave up their Green Lanes access, enabling the new Manor House pub (dated 1931) to be set back 30 feet further from Seven Sisters Road. An island in the middle of the road provided a direct tube-tram interchange, and the width of the road at this point still reflects this feature, long-vanished with the trams themselves.

We have wandered south of our area, into what in 1905 was Stoke Newington, nowadays the London Borough of Hackney. From this junction we can look northwards up Green Lanes to Wood Green, and northeast up Seven Sisters Road to Tottenham, and this focus of so many journeys over the years forms a suitable point to take leave of our own.

(Picture, Dick Whetstone).

111